People of the Old Testament

by **Ruth L. Sprague**
and **Margaret Nixon**
illustrated by **Hugh Price**

United Church Press
BOSTON • PHILADELPHIA

CONTENTS

About This Book

THE STORIES and plays in this book will introduce you to a few of the people of the Old Testament, such as Moses who led the Hebrews out of Egypt where they had been slaves, David who became a great king, and Amos and Jeremiah who spoke out against the injustices and wrongs they saw all around them.

If you would like to read about these people in the Bible itself, look up the references given at the end of each story or play. You will see that some parts of the book follow the Old Testament very closely, but in other parts scenes have been added to the Bible story to make it more understandable.

As you read these stories and plays you will come across some very strange happenings. You will meet an ass that talks and a fish that swallows a man and lands him, alive and well, where God wants him to be. The characters will say things about God and what he does that will not seem quite right to you.

If you try to make the same kind of sense out of this book—or out of the Old Testament itself—that you make out of a history book or a newspaper, you may have all kinds of trouble, and you will miss some fun! On the other hand, if you keep in mind a few ideas about what the Old Testament is, you will be better able to enjoy and understand this book.

The Old Testament is the story of the Hebrew people through many generations. It contains the folktales, legends, and songs of these people, as well as their history. Reading the Bible is a little bit like reading a history book in which tales about George Washington, like the one about his chopping down a cherry tree, are all mixed up with the story of what he actually did as the first president of the United States.

Some parts of the Bible—the story about Jonah and the fish, for example—are fiction. Such stories say something important about God or about people, but they are not meant to be history.

Even the parts of the Bible that do tell about events that happened, or that probably happened, are different from other history books. The people who told the stories in the Bible were not just telling about the great people and the great events of their past. They were telling about *their God*. They were telling the story of his bringing them out of Egypt and making them into a nation, of his promise to be their God always and their promise to be faithful to him, of their breaking the promise over and over again, and of God's trying over and over again to bring them back to him.

Almost everything that happened to the people of the Old Testament said something to them about God. And this is why the Bible is so important to us. It is about our God. In the Bible we see what God does among men. We see him right in the midst of what happens in the world. We see how much he cares about men, and we see him trying always to bring his people back to him when they forget about him. In the Old Testament we are seeing God through the eyes of the Hebrew people, to be sure, and we need to remember this. But it is our God we are seeing.

And we see ourselves! In telling their story about what God had done among them, the Hebrew people were amazingly honest about themselves. Because they were, the Bible shows us how great and how foolish men can be. It helps us to see ourselves as God's children; it helps us to see how often we fail to be what God wants us to be; and it helps us to laugh at ourselves.

The Man Who Had to Flee His Country

THE HEBREW people were slaves in the land of Egypt for many years. One Hebrew child, whose name was Moses, grew up in the royal palace and was treated just as if he were an Egyptian prince. But Moses did not forget that he was really a Hebrew.

CHARACTERS: MOSES

EGYPTIAN OVERSEER

SLAVE

SHEMUEL } Hebrew slaves
NADAB

ZIPPORAH, ABIGAIL, and five other daughters of Jethro

TWO SHEPHERDS

JETHRO

SCENE ONE

Moses, dressed in the garb of an Egyptian prince, walks through a city in Egypt where the Hebrew slaves are constructing new buildings and roads. Egyptian overseers watch the slaves and beat them if they stop their work even for a moment.

MOSES (*speaking to himself*):   I can't stand this! The way these slaves are forced to work makes me fighting angry. Carrying those heavy loads is the work of animals! Then they're beaten if they so much as stop to catch their breath. And they are my Hebrew brothers! I'd be right here working, too, if I hadn't been raised in the pharaoh's palace. These slaves would never dream that I care about the way they're treated. Seeing me walk around in my fine clothes, they'd never imagine that I'm one of them.

1

As Moses walks along he comes to an almost deserted building. Behind it he sees a Hebrew slave and an Egyptian overseer. The slave has apparently been sent to bring some materials from a small storehouse at the rear of the building, and the overseer is checking up on him. All the other slaves and their overseers are at the front of the building. As Moses approaches them the Egyptian speaks to the slave.

EGYPTIAN: Hurry up, you worthless one. You were told to *run* to the storehouse, not walk! (*He hits the slave with a whip.*)

SLAVE (*crying out in pain*): O God, save us from these beasts!

EGYPTIAN (*hitting the slave again and again*): Beasts, are we? Take that and that and that . . .

MOSES: Stop! I command you to stop.

EGYPTIAN (*turning in surprise and looking at Moses*): Who are you?

MOSES: I command you to stop!

EGYPTIAN: I see by your robe that you are an Egyptian, but who are you to shout orders to me?

MOSES: Never mind who I am. I command you to stop.

EGYPTIAN: Only after I have beaten this useless slave to a pulp. (*He turns to the slave, who is now down on one knee, and lashes him again.*)

MOSES (*shouting*): If you do not stop I will kill you!

EGYPTIAN: You speak boldly. What is this slave to you? (*He goes on beating the man.*)

MOSES: He is one of my Hebrew brothers. Stop beating him, I tell you!

Ignoring Moses, the Egyptian raises the whip again. Moses stoops to pick up a large rock on the ground before him. The Egyptian turns to watch Moses, and the slave slips away. With a mighty swing Moses heaves the rock at the head of the Egyptian. It strikes him on the forehead, and he immediately collapses to the ground. Moses steps cautiously toward him, draws back, and then bends over him.

MOSES: He is dead! I've killed him! What will happen now? Did anyone see me? (*He looks around but sees no one.*) What should I do with him? I must get rid of the body quickly. (*He picks up a large stick, digs a hole in the sand, and pushes the body of the Egyptian into it. Then he quickly fills the hole and flees to his home.*)

SCENE TWO

The next day. Moses has returned to the place where he killed the Egyptian to make certain that the body is still safely buried in the sand. As he enters two Hebrew slaves are fighting with each other. He runs to them and separates them.

MOSES (*speaking to the one who started the fight*): My brother, why do you strike your fellow? Isn't your life hard enough without fighting each other?

SHEMUEL: What business is it of yours, Egyptian?

NADAB: We can take care of our own fights without you. Who made you a judge over us?

MOSES: Brothers, I'm not trying to judge over you; I'm pleading with you to stop your fighting.

NADAB: What if we refuse? Will you kill us as you killed the Egyptian yesterday?

MOSES: What are you saying?

SHEMUEL: Are you surprised to know that we saw you?

MOSES: I don't know what you mean!

SHEMUEL: That slave the Egyptian was beating saw the whole thing. He watched you kill that man and then dig a hole and bury him.

NADAB: It will go hard with you, Egyptian, killing one of your own people.

MOSES (*talking to himself*): Do the Egyptians know? Has the pharaoh himself heard? If he does I will be put to death. I must hide. (*With a final glance at the Hebrew slaves he turns and runs.*)

3

SCENE THREE

The land of Midian where Moses has been wandering since he fled from Egypt. He is sitting on a rock close by a well where he has stopped for a drink of cool water. Seven women enter, followed by a flock of sheep. They draw water from the well and pour it into troughs. As they do so, two rough-looking men shepherds enter with a large flock of sheep following them.

FIRST SHEPHERD: Move away, women. (*He pushes several of them from the well.*) We cannot wait for your sheep to drink. We have our own that must be watered. We are busy men.

ZIPPORAH: We were here first. Besides, we've already partly filled the troughs for our flock. You can't . . .

SECOND SHEPHERD: Away with you, woman!

FIRST SHEPHERD (*driving the sheep that belong to the women away from the troughs*): Away, away!

ABIGAIL (*turning helplessly to her sisters*): What can we do? They are using the water *we* have drawn for *their* sheep.

MOSES (*rising and striding over to the well*): What's happening here?

ZIPPORAH: We have drawn water for our sheep, and now these men are using it.

MOSES (*speaking to the shepherds*): You! Move your sheep away! This water belongs to the women. Quickly, drive your sheep away!

SECOND SHEPHERD: Who gives you the right to tell us what to do?

MOSES (*suddenly lashing out in anger and swinging his staff at the heads of the shepherds*): Move your sheep away!

The shepherds, realizing that this is a furious man, retreat with their flock.

ZIPPORAH (*to Moses as she continues to draw water*): We are very grateful to you for driving the men away.

MOSES: Here, let me help you. (*He carries the water to the trough.*)

4

ABIGAIL: Those men often come here just at this time, when they know we are watering our flocks, and use the water we have drawn.

MOSES: It makes my blood boil to see such behavior. I don't understand how people can be so unfair!

SCENE FOUR

Same as Scene Three. Moses is sitting by the well, resting. Zipporah enters and walks quickly up to him.

ZIPPORAH: Oh, you're still here. I'm so glad. I was afraid you might have left. My father wants you to come and eat bread with us.

MOSES: That is very kind of him.

ZIPPORAH: We should have invited you before. When we told our father that an Egyptian had helped us by driving away the shepherds, he asked, "Where is he? Why didn't you bring him with you?" My father always welcomes strangers. We should have known this and brought you home with us, instead of leaving you to sit here alone.

MOSES (*rising and walking along with Zipporah*): Your father must be a good man. What is his name?

ZIPPORAH: He is Jethro, the priest of Midian. The seven of us who were drawing the water are his daughters. We all welcome you to our home.

SCENE FIVE

Several years later. Moses and Zipporah are married. Jethro is sitting on a rock outside his house. Moses enters.

MOSES: Greetings! (*He sits down on the ground facing Jethro.*)

JETHRO: Greetings, my son. You must be very tired from these many days out with the sheep. Did you find good places for grazing? And are all the sheep safe?

MOSES: The sheep? Oh, yes, they're fine. Yes, the sheep are safe, all of them.

JETHRO (*looking intently at Moses*): Is something wrong, Moses? What's on your mind?

MOSES (*taking a deep breath*): Jethro, my father, for some years now I have lived here and tended your sheep. I have been content, even though I have often thought of Egypt, of my life there, and of my Hebrew brothers who are slaves. Until today, I had not thought seriously of going back. But now I have come to ask your permission to leave.

JETHRO (*obviously startled by Moses' announcement*): What makes you think you want to leave Midian? You might not be safe in Egypt. Someone might recognize you and remember that you killed an Egyptian overseer. Besides, what could you do there?

MOSES: I know there is danger. But the suffering of my people is great. The present pharaoh is even more cruel than the previous one.

JETHRO: Yes, I've heard this. But what can *you* do about it?

MOSES: I must go to the pharaoh and tell him to let my people go.

JETHRO (*looking at Moses in amazement*): What?

MOSES: I know my words sound strange. They sound strange to me too. But I know I must do this. The Lord God has called me. He will set my people free. I am to go to the pharaoh and tell him to let the Hebrew slaves go. Then I am to lead the people out of Egypt.

JETHRO: Where did you get this idea? How do you know that God is going to do this?

MOSES: I will have to tell you all that has happened. Then perhaps you will understand. I was leading the sheep up Mount Sinai, looking for better grazing land. My mind was on Egypt at the time and on the suffering of the slaves. Suddenly I came upon a bush that was aflame. Curious and somewhat startled, I walked toward the bush, and as I did so, God spoke to me. He said, "I have seen the suffering of my people who are slaves in Egypt. I will deliver them from their cruel masters and bring them to a good land that will be their own." Then God called *me* to go to the pharaoh to tell him to let the people go.

JETHRO: And this was God who was telling you this?

MOSES: Yes. I wondered if my Hebrew brothers would listen to me and believe that God would bring them out of Egypt. Surely they would ask me God's name so that they would know who sent me. God answered me, saying, "I am who I am; I cause to happen what happens. And when you speak to the Hebrew people, tell them that the God of their fathers sent you."

JETHRO: But how will you persuade the pharaoh to let your people go? He won't give up the slaves easily.

MOSES: God will help me. He will be with me. I protested at first when God called me to do this, because I am slow of speech. Besides, I was frightened and I wanted God to send somebody else. But God said he would be with me.

JETHRO (*shaking his head slowly*): Your task will be difficult!

MOSES: Yes, I know that. But the Lord God has called me to it, and I cannot refuse. With your permission I shall leave tomorrow, taking my wife and sons with me.

JETHRO: I can see that you are determined, so I shall not try to stop you. Go in peace.

Exodus 2:11—4:20

In the Desert

Moses led the Hebrew people out of Egypt toward the land God promised to them. For many years they lived in the desert. They had a hard life and a hard time learning to be God's faithful people.

CHARACTERS: REUBEN ⎫
                HAMUL ⎬ Hebrew men
                ASHER ⎭

                AARON, Moses' brother
                OTHER HEBREWS
                MOSES

                NOAH ⎫
                LABAN ⎬ Hebrew men

                A YOUNG MAN
                JETHRO

SCENE ONE

The desert, not far from Mount Sinai where the Hebrew people are encamped some time after their deliverance from Egypt. A group of men sit on the ground talking.

REUBEN: If only we were back in Egypt! Our children weren't hungry there. Just look at my son over there crying for bread, and I haven't any to give him.

HAMUL (*nodding in agreement*): There was always plenty of bread in Egypt. Even though we were slaves we were better off than we are here in the desert.

REUBEN (*sneering*): Moses said he was bringing us to a broad and good land! Well, the land is broad all right—broad desert! He brought us out here to die, all of us.

ASHER: But maybe the Lord will do something. When we didn't have any water, Moses called upon the Lord to help us, and he did.

REUBEN: Well, he certainly isn't doing anything for us now.

HAMUL: For that matter, we don't have any too much water either. We've had nothing but trouble ever since we came out of Egypt.

ASHER: I don't remember that we had an easy time of it in Egypt. Perhaps my memory fails me.

REUBEN: I didn't say that things were easy in Egypt. But was the lash of the overseer's whip worse than seeing your children go without bread? We never should have listened to Moses. We shouldn't have believed all his fine promises. It's better to live as slaves in a rich land than starve to death in the desert.

HAMUL: Shhh, here comes Aaron. Don't let him hear your complaining or he'll tell his brother.

AARON (*walks up to the men*): The whole congregation is gathering to hear the word of the Lord. Tell everyone to come to Moses' tent.

The men get up and help Aaron spread word of the meeting.

SCENE TWO

An open space near Moses' tent where all the people are assembled. Moses and Aaron step before the gathering, and Aaron addresses the people.

AARON: The Lord God has heard the murmuring and the complaining among you. He knows you haven't had enough to eat. The word of the Lord is this: you shall be filled. In the morning there will be bread for everyone.

The people talk among themselves excitedly.

AARON: The Lord says that when you see the food he gives you, then you will know that he is the Lord.

The crowd moves away, each going to his own tent.

ASHER: The Lord God will help us. He gave us water when we were thirsty; now he will give us food.

REUBEN: Maybe so, but there's no place for any food to come from around here.

ASHER: How do you know? You've never lived here before. The Lord will provide food even in the desert.

SCENE THREE

Early the next morning. All the people gather around Aaron and Moses in an area where there are a great many desert shrubs. On the ground all around the bushes is a white substance that looks a little like frost.

THE PEOPLE: What is it?

REUBEN: That white stuff on the ground—what is it? I've never seen it before.

MOSES: It is the bread that God has provided. It is manna. Every morning this manna will be on the ground.

HAMUL (*tasting it*): It is a strange kind of bread! It's sweet, almost like honey.

MOSES: Gather as much of it as you need, each of you. Take enough for every member of your family. Do not leave any of it.

ASHER (*starting to gather the manna*): The Lord is good! He brought us out of Egypt; he gives us water to quench our thirst; now he gives us bread to meet our daily need. He will bring us to the broad and good land he has promised!

REUBEN: Yes, the Lord *is* good.

SCENE FOUR

Many days later. Moses sits in front of his tent judging the cases the people bring before him. Two men are presenting their sides of a quarrel they have had. Other people stand around awaiting their turns.

MOSES: You say this man struck you with a stone because he was angry with you?

NOAH: Yes, and I have not been able to walk these many days because the stone struck my leg.

LABAN: But he was trying to steal from me.

MOSES: What evidence do you have of this?

A young man enters and stands before Moses.

MOSES (*turning to the young man*): What is it? Has something happened?

YOUNG MAN: There is a man coming toward the camp. I met him in the desert, and he sent me ahead to tell you he is coming. He says his name is Jethro.

MOSES: Jethro! My father-in-law! He is coming here? This is wonderful news! I'll go meet him.

SCENE FIVE

A few minutes later, just outside the camp Moses and Jethro run toward each other and embrace.

JETHRO: Moses, my son! I have heard of all that God has done for you. And I heard that your travels had brought you here, not far from Sinai, so I decided to come to you.

MOSES: How are you, my father? Are you well?

JETHRO: Yes, and all my family. Tell me all that has happened, Moses. Tell me how it was in Egypt and how you have managed with all these people here in the desert.

MOSES: I'll tell you everything, Jethro. But first I must go back to the camp and judge the people. They come to me with their quarrels and their troubles, and I act as judge. Come along with me and watch while I listen to the people's problems and tell them God's judgment.

11

SCENE SIX

A short time later. Jethro and Moses are in front of Moses' tent talking.

JETHRO: So the pharaoh would not let you go even though great troubles came upon his land?

MOSES: That's right. Over and over again the Lord showed his power. Locusts, frogs, and gnats came over the land, but still the pharaoh refused to see that these were signs of the power of our God and that he had better let us go before more disasters befell him.

JETHRO: But finally he did let you go. How was that?

MOSES: Several times he said he'd let us go, but then he changed his mind. What finally persuaded him was the death that suddenly came upon hundreds of the young sons of the Egyptians—all the firstborn in the land, including the pharaoh's own son. When this happened the pharaoh came to me and said, "Your God has brought this trouble upon us. Go, take your people. Be gone from this land."

JETHRO: And you were all ready to leave?

MOSES: Yes, all the Hebrew slaves left immediately before daybreak. We took our possessions and left in a hurry before the pharaoh could change his mind. We did not even wait for the leavening and baking of bread but took the unleavened dough with us.

Our troubles weren't over, however. The pharaoh changed his mind, as he had done before, and sent his army after us. But again God came to our aid. He led us across the sea on dry ground. When the Egyptians started across with their chariots, they got stuck in the mud, and the waters rose and drowned them. Once again the Lord our God had saved us.

JETHRO: The Lord has done great things for you, bringing your people out of Egypt as he did. I should like to offer a sacrifice to him in thanksgiving for what he has done.

MOSES: Good. We'll gather all the people, and you will offer the sacrifice. Then the elders and Aaron my brother will eat bread with you. We'll have a great celebration.

12

Scene Seven

Later the same day in an open area outside the camp. People are gathering around the altar on which the sacrifice is to be offered. Small groups of earlycomers are talking.

Asher (*peering over the crowd*):   Here comes Moses. And there's his father-in-law, Jethro. It is good that the priest of Midian is with us to offer a sacrifice to God.

Hamul: It's good to have a sacrifice and a feast! We'll have some meat to eat. I get so sick of manna.

Reuben: But at least you aren't starving. Be grateful to the Lord for that!

Hamul: I am grateful, but I still get tired of eating manna. And I get tired of Moses and his ways. After all, we could have feasts more often!

Reuben: I get tired of Moses, too, with all his strict rules and the way he lords it over us.

Hamul: Worse than that, the judgments he makes aren't fair. Why, just the other day he ruled against me. Enan claimed I had taken more than my share of water. All Moses had to go on was Enan's word, and he took it instead of listening to my side of the story. Who made him judge over us anyway?

Asher: God did, you know that. I think Moses tries to be fair. You're just angry with him because his judgment went against you . . . Oh, look, they're slaying the ram for the sacrifice. Jethro is going to speak.

Jethro: Blessed is the Lord! He brought you who were slaves out from bondage in Egypt. He has led you to this place and will lead you on as he has promised. He is greater and more powerful than all gods. Blessed is the Lord!

Jethro offers the ram as sacrifice. All the people watch the ceremonies and then join in the feast.

14

SCENE EIGHT

The following evening. Jethro and Moses are again sitting in front of Moses' tent.

JETHRO: You must be very tired. Is every day like this one, with people coming to you with their quarrels and problems from morning to night?

MOSES: Yes, many days are like this.

JETHRO: Why do you sit alone as judge and have the people stand for hours waiting their turn?

MOSES: Because the people come to me. Whenever there is any kind of trouble, the people bring it before me. They come to hear the law of God and his judgment.

JETHRO: This is not a good plan. The job is too big for you.

MOSES: But what am I to do? So many problems come up. Living in the desert this way isn't easy. The people are restless. They forget how hard their life was in Egypt, and sometimes they think they'd rather go back there than face the hardships of the desert. They forget all that God has done for them, and they do not trust him. Because they are restless and dissatisfied, they quarrel among themselves.

JETHRO: Let me give you some advice. You and you alone should represent the people before God. You, as their leader, must teach them God's law and show them what God requires of them. But you cannot do everything. Appoint some men to help you. Choose the most able ones, those who are faithful to God and who will not accept bribes, and let them serve as judges. Let them take care of all the little quarrels among the people. When a matter of great importance comes up, the judges should bring it to you, but they should take care of small matters themselves.

MOSES: You are a wise man. I shall do as you say.

15

Scene Nine

Many weeks later in an open space in the encampment.

REUBEN: I tell you, I don't think he'll ever come back. Up there on that mountain anything could happen to him.

HAMUL: But every time Moses has gone up the mountain before, he has returned. He's come back and told us the word of God.

REUBEN: But he's never been gone so long before. I'm sure something has happened to him.

ASHER: What will we do? Without Moses, how will God lead us?

REUBEN: What will happen to us? Here we are stranded in the desert. Who will show us where we should go? We'd better find some gods to lead us. Maybe we can make gods who will take better care of us than Moses did.

HAMUL (*enthusiastically*): Yes! Let's make gods who will give us plenty of food and water and who will take us out of this desert to a good land.

REUBEN: Where is Aaron? If Moses has left us, let's go to Aaron and ask him to make us gods.

Everyone agrees eagerly.

REUBEN: I'll go find Aaron. (*Exits.*)

The group continues to talk excitedly until Reuben returns, bringing Aaron with him.

REUBEN (*to the group*): I have asked Aaron about Moses, and he knows nothing. He, too, thinks something may have happened to him.

AARON: Yes, that's right. Many times Moses has gone up the mountain to meet God, but he has never been gone as long as this. I'm afraid he'll never return.

HAMUL: We've been talking about that and wondering what will happen to us without him. We need some gods to lead us. Otherwise we may be left here to die in the desert.

16

LABAN: Yes, make us gods, Aaron, so that we will not perish here.

REUBEN: Make us gods who will do well by us—give us plenty of food and always lead us to victory over our enemies.

AARON: All right. Send word around the camp that everyone must give all the gold he owns. Tell your wives and sons and daughters to take the rings from their ears. Bring me all the gold you can find.

The men exit and return bringing gold rings to Aaron who mean-while has built a great fire and made a wooden calf.

AARON: Now I shall make a god to lead us. (*He takes the gold and melts it, then coats the wooden figure with the molten metal. When he finishes he stands off from his handiwork and looks at it admiringly.*)

REUBEN (*turning to the others*): Good! Now we have a god to lead us.

LABAN: You have done well, Aaron. He looks like a good god.

AARON (*still admiring the calf*): I declare that tomorrow will be a feast day. I will build an altar before this golden calf, and we shall sac-rifice animals upon it. For the whole day we shall eat, drink, and enjoy ourselves.

CHORUS OF VOICES: A feast day! Good for Aaron! Hurrah!

SCENE TEN

Same place the next day. An altar has been built in front of the calf, and all the people have gathered around, singing and dancing before the altar.

REUBEN: What a great day this is! I haven't eaten so much since we left Egypt.

HAMUL: This god is good to us! He lets us slaughter as many sheep as we want for a feast!

ASHER: Look, look, everybody! Isn't that Moses coming down from the mountain?

HAMUL: It must be. Who else dares to climb the mountain of God? It *is* Moses! What shall we do?

The people try to put out the fire on the altar, but Moses enters before they succeed. He is carrying stone tablets on which there is writing. He stands for a moment taking in the scene. Then, in fierce anger, he throws the tablets to the ground.

MOSES: My people, how could you do this? How could you turn against your God, the God of your fathers who brought you out of Egypt? He has been faithful to his promises! Is this how you respond? You faithless people! How could you do this great evil? (*He goes to the calf and pushes it into the fire. The people draw back behind Aaron.*)

MOSES (*to Aaron*): What happened? What did the people do, that you made this calf for them?

AARON (*shrinking back from his brother*): Don't be angry. You know these people, and you know how often they do evil. They came to me and asked me to make them gods. They thought you would never return, and they were afraid. I asked them to bring all their gold, and they did. Then I threw the gold on the fire and out came this calf. Don't be angry with me, Moses.

MOSES (*to the people*): You have sinned a great sin. Now take the calf, grind it up, and scatter it upon the water. You will have to drink the gold powder! (*Shakes his head sadly.*) How could you do this thing? I shall have to ask the Lord God to forgive you. Your sin is indeed great.

SCENE ELEVEN

Moses is alone outside the encampment, praying to God.

MOSES: O God, forgive these people, for they have done a great wrong. They have made a god out of gold. I know you are angry with them, and I can understand why you are. But remember, you brought them out of Egypt. You promised to be their God. Do not punish them. If you can't forgive them, let me die. (*He is silent for a time; then he rises and walks back toward the camp.*)

Asher, who has walked out from the camp, stands and watches Moses as he approaches. Moses walks with his head down, deep in thought. Suddenly he realizes that someone is nearby and looks up.

MOSES: Asher! You startled me. What are you doing here?

ASHER: I didn't mean to frighten you. I was watching for you. Will God forgive us for what we did? I was so anxious to know that I came out here, thinking I could tell by looking at your face. I didn't mean to bother you.

MOSES: You're a good man, Asher. You are among the few faithful ones. God is angry, so angry that he will not come among his people, because he might destroy them if he did. He will come to us again, and when he does he will punish us. But he will not forsake us. He has told me to go on, to lead the people to the good land that he has promised to us.

ASHER: What we did was a great sin. We broke our promise to be faithful to God. I wouldn't have been surprised if God had forsaken us, but he has kept his promise even though we have broken ours.

MOSES: Yes, he is our God. He will not forsake us. But when will the people learn to obey him? (*Moses is silent for a moment, and then he goes on, this time speaking more to himself than to Asher.*) Will these people ever learn to trust him, and him only? Will they ever stop their complaining and their quarreling and learn to live together as a community? Will they ever keep their promise to be God's faithful people?

Exodus 12:29–34; 14:5–30; 16:1–21; 18; 32

A Faithful Prophet
and His Faithful Ass

THE KING of Moab was frightened. The Hebrew people, the Israelites, had set up camp on the plains of Moab. These people had defeated the Amorites and taken their land, and now they were in Moab.

"What shall we do?" Balak, the king, asked his advisors and princes. "Look at what happened to the Amorites. Why, those Israelites will lick up everything around us just as an ox licks up grass!"

Balak's advisors tried to think what the king should do. "I have an idea," one of them said. "Send to Balaam, that great prophet. Have him come here and curse the Israelites. Then they will not be able to win any battles."

The king and all his advisors agreed that this was the thing to do. "Tell Balaam that a people has come out of Egypt, and they are taking all the land around here," the king said to the princes he chose as messengers. "Ask him to come and curse these Israelites, because they are too strong for us, and we shall not be able to drive them away. Offer him whatever fees he asks."

The messengers set out, taking many gifts with them. When they reached Balaam they explained their errand, saying, "We know that the people you bless are truly blessed and those whom you curse are truly cursed. If you curse the Israelites, they cannot possibly defeat us and take our land."

Balaam said to the messengers, "Stay here tonight, and I will give you word in the morning. I cannot answer now. I will have to see what the Lord says about this."

That night the Lord came to Balaam and asked, "Who are these men?"

Balaam explained who they were and why they had come. "They want me to curse those Israelites who have come out of Egypt and are now overrunning the whole land."

"Don't go with them," God said. "Those Israelites are blessed. Do not curse them."

The next morning Balaam went to the messengers who had come from King Balak. "Go back to Moab," he said. "The Lord will not let me go with you."

Greatly disappointed, the messengers returned to the king and told him that Balaam refused to come. "Go right back," King Balak told the men. "I'll send other princes with you, and more gifts. Tell Balaam I'll do anything he asks, but let nothing stop him from coming here and cursing the Israelites."

"No matter how much you pay me, I will not disobey the Lord," Balaam said to the messengers and princes when they came before him and showed him the many gifts Balak had sent. "But stay here tonight, and I'll see what the Lord will say to me."

Once again God came to Balaam in the night. This time he said, "You may go with them, but do only what I tell you to do and nothing more."

Early the next morning Balaam went out and saddled his ass and set off for Moab. The princes and messengers went first, making a very fine procession. Balaam followed, riding on the ass that had served him faithfully for many years.

Suddenly the ass saw an angel of the Lord standing right in the middle of the road, holding up a sword as a signal to stop. Because the ass knew she must obey an angel of the Lord, she immediately turned aside into the vineyard.

Annoyed that his faithful ass would turn off the road without being told to do so, Balaam struck her with his staff. The ass started to turn back toward the road, but the angel stepped in front of her once again, this time in a narrow place between two walls. The ass backed up, pushing against the wall and crushing Balaam's foot. Thoroughly angry with his ass by this time, Balaam struck her hard and ordered her to go ahead.

The ass had gone only a few steps when the angel once again stood in front of her. This time the path was so narrow that the ass could not turn aside. So she did the only thing she could do: she lay down right where she was, with Balaam still sitting on her. By now Balaam was so angry that he took his staff and struck her as hard as he could—once, twice, three times.

The poor ass lay there, hurt and confused. What could she do? She *had* to obey the angel of the Lord. Why couldn't her master see the angel? Why was he beating her when all she was doing was keeping him from disobeying the angel? Slowly the ass raised her head and opened her mouth. The Lord had given her the power of speech! "What have I done?" asked the ass. "Why have you hit me these three times?"

Balaam answered, "Because you've made fun of me, lying down under me this way. Why, if I had a sword handy, I'd kill you!"

This was too much. The ass had no more patience. "Look here," she said, "am I not the ass you've ridden for all these years? Did I ever do anything like this before?"

"Well, no," Balaam answered timidly. He could make no sense out of what was happening. But just at that moment the Lord opened Balaam's eyes so that he, too, could see the angel. Now Balaam understood. He fell down before the angel.

"Why have you beaten your poor ass this way?" the angel asked. "I've come to warn you about going to Moab. The ass saw me, and she knew enough to turn aside."

"I didn't know you were standing in the road," Balaam explained. "If this trip to Moab is wrong, I'll go back home."

"No, you may go with the men. But be careful. Say only what the Lord tells you to say."

Balaam and his ass continued down the road to Moab. Before they reached the city, Balak came out to meet them.

"Why didn't you come when I sent for you the first time?" Balak asked the prophet. "Didn't you know how much I'd be willing to give you for cursing the people of Israel?"

Balaam answered, "I've come this time, but I shall speak only what the Lord tells me to speak."

The next day Balak took the prophet up a mountain where Balaam could see the Israelite camp. "Build me seven altars and bring animals to sacrifice on them," Balaam said. "Perhaps the Lord will come and tell me what I should say."

The king did as Balaam requested. When the sacrifices had been offered, Balaam said to God, "I've prepared seven altars and offered sacrifices on each. Now tell me what I'm to say."

God answered, "Say to Balak that you cannot curse Israel. How can you curse her when I have not cursed her? Bless her; do not curse her."

Balaam repeated God's word to Balak. "What have you done to me?" the king asked. "Here you are supposed to curse my enemies, but instead you bless them."

"I can only do what God tells me to do," Balaam answered.

24

"Well, let's go to another mountain and build more altars," the king suggested. "Come to another place where you can see those Israelites. Then curse them for me."

Balaam and Balak went to another mountain and built seven altars. "You stand here by the burnt offering," Balaam told the king, "and I'll go meet the Lord over there."

After a time Balaam came back. "What has the Lord said this time?" Balak asked.

Balaam answered, "The Lord says, 'I have blessed these people and I cannot take back my blessing. Therefore you must not curse them. You must bless them instead.'"

Balak was disgusted. "If you can't curse them, at least don't bless them!"

"But I told you, I can only speak the words the Lord puts in my mouth," Balaam reminded him.

"Well, come then, and I'll take you to another place," the king said. "Maybe God will let you curse the Israelites from there."

The two men climbed another mountain, built seven altars, and made seven sacrifices.

Balaam looked out over the plain and saw the Israelites encamped there. God's spirit came upon him. "These are the people God brought out of Egypt," Balaam said. "Blessed be everyone who blesses them, and cursed be those who curse them. This is the word of the Lord."

Now Balak was furious. "I called you to curse my enemies, and three times now you've blessed them instead. Now go—before you do any more harm."

Balaam responded, "From the beginning I have said that I must speak what God tells me. I told the messengers when they first came to me that no matter what gifts you offered, even a whole house full of silver and gold, I would not say anything except the words God told me to say."

Once again Balaam repeated his blessing of the people of Israel. Then he saddled his faithful ass and went back to his own city.

Numbers 22—24

Joshua Makes a Treaty

"WE'VE GOT to stop them. We've got to stop that man Joshua and all his people from taking our land!"

"But how? One city after another has fallen into their hands."

"Many kings are gathering to fight against Joshua. I think we should join them."

The leaders of Gibeon had been talking like this for a long time. Their land would probably be invaded at almost any time by the Israelites who had gradually been taking over all the territory around them. Sometimes these Hebrew people simply settled on the land. But if there was resistance to them or if they wanted the city, their armies, under Joshua, would come in and conquer. Gibeon did not have a king, but it had powerful warriors. Should it hold out against Joshua? Should it join with other small kingdoms nearby and fight the Israelites? Or should it let the Hebrew people take over peacefully, and hope the city would not be destroyed?

"It won't do any good to make an alliance with other cities and their kings," one man argued. "Joshua will defeat us all and destroy us. I don't understand how he does it. His God must be more powerful than all the other gods put together!"

"I agree," another man spoke up. "We'd better make some kind of treaty with Joshua and not risk fighting him."

But others did not agree. One man said, "What kind of treaty could you make with him? Not one that would do us any good! He won't agree to let our land alone if he happens to want it."

"He might agree never to make war on us and to be our ally if we ever got into a war with anybody else." The man who had suggested the treaty earlier was defending his idea.

27

"That's ridiculous!" his opponents argued. "Joshua's not going to agree to let us alone when he's on our doorstep right now. Sure, he might like to have some friends and allies, but not from the very territory he's probably planning to invade next. Use your head! Would you make such a treaty if you were in his shoes?"

"No, I guess not," the man who made the suggestion agreed sheepishly.

"But that gives me an idea. I know what we should do." Everyone turned to the man who spoke, so he stood up to present his plan.

"If Joshua thought we were people from a distant place, he would make a treaty with us, because he'd have nothing to lose. He might agree to live at peace with us and be our ally. It wouldn't be a bad idea to have Joshua and that powerful God on our side!"

"I don't see what you're getting at. We aren't from a distant land. We're from right here, right where the Israelites are going to settle."

"But we can trick them, and that's my idea. We can go to Joshua and tell him that we're from a distant country. We can make ourselves look as if we had traveled for a long, long time."

"But that won't stop his people from settling on our land."

"No," admitted the man who had thought of the plan, "and Joshua will be angry when he finds out who we are. But he won't be able to make war against us and destroy us. That's the important thing."

So the men talked and finally agreed on their strategy. Those appointed to go to Joshua put on tattered clothing and patched sandals. Old wine skins and worn-out sacks were loaded on asses. Provisions were placed in the sacks—moldy food and bread. As the men started out, they did indeed look as if they had been traveling for many, many days.

The men went straight to Joshua's camp at Gilgal. The leader of the Gibeonites said, "We have come from a far country, but we have heard of you. Make a treaty with us."

Joshua and the men with him listened carefully. "How do we know that you come from a far country?" Joshua asked. "Perhaps you live among us. If you do, how could we make a treaty with you?"

The leader of the Gibeonites answered, "We are your servants."

"But *who* are you?" Joshua asked impatiently.

"We have come from a very far country. Your fame and the fame of your God have come to us by report over a great distance. We have heard of all your God did in Egypt, and we know that you have won many victories in the land of Canaan. The leaders of our country told us to take provisions and come to you. See, here is our bread. It was still warm, fresh from the ovens, when we started on our journey. But now look at it—dry and moldy. We started out with new wine skins. See how old they are now? And see how our garments are torn?"

"All right," Joshua said. "I believe you. We will make a treaty with you. Always there will be peace between us. We will never destroy your city. We swear before our God that we will let you live."

The Israelites and the Gibeonites joined in a common meal to mark the completion of the treaty. Then the men from Gibeon returned to their homes, very much pleased with the success of their plan.

After a few days the Israelites went on with their conquest of the land. Soon they moved into Gibeon where the first people they saw were the men who had come to Gilgal to make a peace treaty. They had been tricked!

The Israelites knew that they could not break the treaty, even though they had been tricked into making it. When the Hebrew warriors heard that they could not take the city by force and kill the people as they had done elsewhere, they became angry with their leaders. But Joshua and the others said, "We have sworn to these people by the Lord, the God of Israel, so now we cannot touch them."

Joshua then called all the men of Gibeon to him. "Why did you deceive us?" he asked angrily. "Why did you say you came from a distant country when you live right here among us?"

The Gibeonite spokesman answered, "Because we knew you intended to conquer the land, we were afraid. We heard that your God had given it to you, and that your people were settling among us. We feared that you might destroy us. Now we are at your mercy. Do to us what seems good and right to you."

Joshua answered, "We have made a treaty before our God. We cannot take your lives nor destroy your city. But because you deceived us we will make you servants. Some of your men must always provide water for our people and wood for the altar on which we sacrifice to our God."

Many days passed. Some of the Israelites settled in Gibeon, and the Gibeonites remained in their city and served them as Joshua had ordered. Joshua himself and all the warriors remained at their camp in Gilgal.

Meanwhile the kings of some of the cities nearby, already afraid of Joshua, heard of what had happened in Gibeon. Gibeon was a great city; it was like a royal city even though it did not have a king. Its warriors were famous for their skill and courage. To have this city make a treaty with Joshua instead of fighting him made the other kings angry and frightened. They had counted on Gibeon to help them defend themselves against Joshua and his armies. The king of Jerusalem became so angry that he sent word to all the other kings, saying, "Let us meet and go to war against Gibeon, for it has made peace with Joshua and with the people of Israel."

The armies gathered, set up camp, and began their attack. Immediately the men of Gibeon sent word to Joshua. "Come to us quickly," they said. "The armies from all around have gathered against us and are making war on us."

Joshua gathered his men together. "The men of Gibeon are in trouble. As God has been faithful to the promise he made to be our God, so we must keep the promises we made to the men of Gibeon. Because we have made a treaty with them, we must go and help them."

All night long the Israelite warriors marched up the steep road from Gilgal to Gibeon. Without stopping to rest they made their attack upon the armies of the kings. The attack was so sudden that the armies fled in panic. The Israelites chased them, and many were killed.

When the battle was over, Joshua and his men raised their voices in praise to God. So much was accomplished in one day that they could

scarcely believe what had happened. "God made the sun stand still for us," Joshua said. "Never has there been a day like this."

The men of Gibeon rejoiced in the victory. Joshua had stood by his treaty with them, even though they had tricked him into making it. And he had won the battle.

"Joshua and his men are great warriors," said one man of Gibeon.

"And their God is a mighty God," added another.

"He is a strange God." The man who spoke had been silent up to now, as if he had been puzzling over the day's events. "Joshua says that the Israelites have come here because their God promised them a broad and good land. He says that they were faithful to the treaty because it was made before their God. And he says that the praise for all their victories must go to this God. Everything that happens to them seems to have something to do with their Lord. He is a strange and mighty God!"

Joshua 9:1—10:15

David Kills the Giant

THE PEOPLE of Israel were at war with the Philistines. Saul, the king of the Israelites, led them in battle, with his son Jonathan assisting him. The three oldest sons of Jesse of Bethlehem were warriors for King Saul, but David, a very young man, had to stay at home and care for the sheep—until the day he went to see his brothers.

CHARACTERS: DAVID
THE BAGGAGE KEEPER
ELIAB
ABINADAB } David's brothers
SHAMMAH
GOLIATH, the Philistine giant
OTHER ISRAELITE WARRIORS
A SERVANT OF KING SAUL
KING SAUL
JONATHAN, the king's son

SCENE ONE

The edge of the camp of the Israelite army. The men are preparing for battle, shouting war cries and getting ready to go against the Philistines. Off to one side is a place where supplies are kept. The young man David enters. He looks around and runs over to the man in charge of supplies as if he is in a hurry to do his errand so that he can watch the preparations for battle.

DAVID: Here is food for my brothers, Eliab, Abinadab, and Shammah. Will you keep it for them?

THE BAGGAGE KEEPER: Yes, I know who they are. I'll see to it that they get it when the battle is over.

DAVID (*handing the man a supply of grain and ten loaves of bread*): That's very good of you.

He dashes off toward the army and works his way in and out among the men until he finds his brothers.

DAVID: There you are. I was looking for you.

ELIAB (*surprised to see David*): What are you doing here?

DAVID: I brought some bread and grain for you. I left it with the baggage keeper. What's going on? Are you about to go into battle?

ELIAB: You're supposed to be looking after the sheep. Who's taking care of them?

DAVID (*annoyed*): Our father sent me here. I didn't just come on my own. I was with the sheep, and he called me and told me to bring food to you and to find out how you were getting along.

There is a good deal of commotion and noise as David finishes his speech. Everyone's attention turns to a giant Philistine who is approaching King Saul. The giant Goliath stands on the hillside and shouts across to Saul and his men.

GOLIATH: Why are you drawn up for battle this way? Choose *one* man from your army and have him come over here and fight with me. Let the battle be between us, not between whole armies. If the man you choose is able to kill me, then you Israelites will be the victors. But if I kill your man, then we Philistines will have won, and you will become our servants. I dare you to send a man out to fight with me!

The Israelites draw back from the giant. There is great murmuring among them, and Saul does not appear to know what to do. As he consults with his son Jonathan and others, the Israelite warriors talk among themselves.

SHAMMAH: Who would fight such a man? He must be ten feet tall!

ABINADAB: Look at the armor he's wearing! You'd never be able to kill him!

ANOTHER WARRIOR: And that spear he's carrying! I wouldn't want to come near him!

DAVID (*to the man who has just spoken*): What would the reward be for fighting this man? Who is he anyway? And how does he dare defy the armies of the God of Israel?

WARRIOR: Anyone who kills him would be well rewarded by King Saul, I'm sure. He'd be given great riches and probably the king's daughter also. (*He looks David up and down.*) Why do you ask? You certainly aren't thinking of fighting Goliath, are you?

ELIAB (*to David*): You're supposed to be at home tending the sheep. You came here only because you wanted to watch the battle. You don't belong around here. This is a place for men—strong ones!

DAVID: I was only asking a question. (*Walks away but stops near another group of men.*)

ISRAELITE WARRIOR: Saul is going to have a hard time finding anyone to fight Goliath. Nobody will fight a giant!

DAVID: What will be the reward for a person who kills the Philistine giant?

WARRIOR: Great riches, I'm sure, but who would take the chance of fighting with him? I certainly wouldn't.

The men go on talking as David moves away, but before he has gone far, a servant of the king comes up to him.

THE KING'S SERVANT: Are you the man who has been asking about the reward for killing Goliath?

DAVID (*surprised*): Yes, I have been asking that question.

SERVANT: Come with me, then. The king wants to talk to you.

SCENE TWO

A few minutes later in another part of the camp. King Saul stands in the center of a group of men. His son Jonathan is beside him.

KING SAUL: You are the man who has been asking about the rewards for killing the giant?

DAVID: Yes, I am. We must not be afraid of that Philistine. I will go and fight him.

KING SAUL (*looking at David carefully*): You can't fight him. You're much too young. You're scarcely more than a boy, and he's a seasoned warrior.

DAVID: But I have fought wild animals many times as I kept the sheep for my father. I have killed lions and bears, and I can kill this Philistine who has defied the armies of the God of Israel.

SAUL: You speak bravely.

JONATHAN: We must send someone to fight. We can't let this Philistine disgrace us.

SAUL: Yes, we must send someone. (*Turns to David.*) Go ahead and fight him, and the Lord be with you. Here, you had better put on my armor to protect you.

David puts on the king's armor and helmet and starts off toward Goliath, but he can scarcely move.

DAVID: I can't wear this. It's too big. Besides, I'm not used to fighting in armor and using a sword. I will fight with stones, shot from this sling. (*Holds up the sling he has with him, then stoops to pick up stones which he puts into his shepherd's bag.*)

SCENE THREE

A few minutes later in a place between the two armies. Goliath stands waiting for the Israelite who is to fight with him. Young David enters.

GOLIATH: Ha! So this is the one who is to fight with me! Am I a dog, that you intend to kill me with those stones? (*Grins at David.*) Come along. I'll see to it that the birds and beasts eat your flesh! The gods have cursed you—all the gods of the Philistines curse you.

DAVID: You come with your sword and spear, but I come in the name of the God of the armies of Israel. I will strike you down and cut off your head! I'll give *your* body to the birds and beasts! The victory will be ours—then all the world will know that there is a God in Israel.

The two men move toward each other. David takes a stone from his bag, puts it in the sling, and swings it around his head several times. The stone flies toward Goliath and strikes him on the forehead. As the giant falls to the ground, David runs over to him, takes the Philistine's sword from him, and cuts off his head. A great cry of joy goes up from the armies of Israel, and they chase the Philistine army out of the land.

SAUL (*coming up to David who is still holding Goliath's head in his hand*):   You have done well, young man. You have won a great victory for us. Tell me, whose son are you?

DAVID: I am the son of Jesse, of Bethlehem.

SAUL: You are a fine warrior. Don't go back to your father's house, but stay with me, and be part of the royal household.

JONATHAN: Yes, come. You will be like a brother to me.

1 Samuel 17:1—18:2

Two Friends

AFTER killing the giant, David remained in the service of King Saul, lived in the royal household, and went to war with the king. He became a very close friend of the king's son Jonathan, but because David won many military victories, Saul became insanely jealous of him.

CHARACTERS: DAVID
JONATHAN
SAUL
A YOUNG BOY

SCENE ONE

Jonathan's room at Saul's headquarters. Jonathan is looking out the window as David rushes in.

DAVID: Jonathan, what have I done? Your father tried to kill me!

JONATHAN (*turning quickly from the window*): What are you saying?

DAVID: It's true. He tried to kill me. I was playing the lyre for him as I sometimes do when he is tired or upset. All of a sudden he heaved his spear at me! I dodged and ran away. But why does Saul want to kill me? What wrong have I done?

JONATHAN: This can't be so! My father hides nothing from me. If he is angry with you, he surely would have told me. You must be mistaken.

DAVID: This is not the first time I've suspected your father. When we returned from battle a few days ago, the women of the villages came out

and gathered in the streets as we marched along. They sang,

> "Saul has slain his thousands,
> And David his ten thousands."

Out of the corner of my eye I watched your father, and I have never
seen such a look of anger on the face of any man.

JONATHAN: David, you're imagining things!

DAVID: I don't think so. Your father knows well that I have found favor with you. He knows you would be grieved if you knew how he feels about me, so he has not told you. But as the Lord lives, Jonathan, there is but a step between me and death.

JONATHAN: What can I do to help you?

DAVID: Tomorrow is the feast of the new moon. I will not come to eat with Saul and you and the others as I usually do. Instead, I will hide myself in the field.

JONATHAN: Yes.

DAVID: If your father misses me and asks you where I am, tell him I have gone to Bethlehem, the city of my birth, to make a sacrifice and join in a family celebration. If he says, "Good," this will show that he feels kindly toward me. But if he is angry—if a little thing like my not being there upsets him—he means evil toward me. Keep faith with me, Jonathan, and if I have done anything wrong, slay me yourself.

JONATHAN: I will keep faith, David, and I will tell you if my father intends to harm you.

DAVID: Good. Who will tell me how your father reacts?

JONATHAN: Three days from now, hide yourself behind the stone heap in the field just outside the city. I will come to the field and shoot three arrows toward the stones. I will have a young lad with me to chase them. If I shout to him, "Look, the arrows are on this side of you; take them," then you are to come, for as the Lord lives, you are safe. But if I say to the youth, "Look, the arrows are beyond you," then go, for the Lord has sent you away. Whatever happens, this matter we've been talking about will be a secret between us forever.

SCENE TWO

The dining room of the king's headquarters two days later.

SAUL: Jonathan, why hasn't David come to dinner either yesterday or today? Where is he?

39

JONATHAN: He has gone to Bethlehem. He asked my permission to leave.

SAUL: For what purpose?

JONATHAN: His family is holding a sacrifice there.

SAUL (*suddenly becoming angry*): You're no son of mine! Don't you realize what you're doing? I know that you and David have become friends, but don't you see that as long as he lives he will be the king, and you will not? Send and bring him to me, and I will have him put to death!

JONATHAN: Why? What has he done?

Saul rises from the table and hurls his spear toward Jonathan. Jonathan angrily leaves the room.

SCENE THREE

The next day. Jonathan and a young lad are in the field just outside the city. Taking an arrow from his bag, Jonathan shoots it toward a heap of rocks where David is hiding. As he starts to shoot, he speaks to the boy.

JONATHAN: Run and find the arrows I shoot.

The boy runs toward the rocks and Jonathan shoots an arrow well beyond him.

JONATHAN: Isn't the arrow beyond you? Hurry, lad, pick it up.

The boy picks up the arrow and brings it back to Jonathan.

JONATHAN: Now take the bow and the arrows back to the city.

The lad leaves. As he does so, David rises from behind the rocks and comes toward Jonathan, weeping.

JONATHAN: David, go now in peace. Remember we have pledged our friendship before the Lord. He will be between us and between our children and our children's children forever.

DAVID: So shall it be!

David departs, and Jonathan goes back into the city.

1 Samuel 19:8–10; 20:1–42

David Becomes King

David escaped from Saul, and for some years he lived as an outlaw, gradually building up a large force of men. By making raids and by promising protection to various towns, he and his followers made their living and gained in power. Saul became increasingly sure that David was a threat to him, and he was determined to kill him.

CHARACTERS: Saul
A Ziphite
Abner, Ahijah, and other advisors to King Saul
David
Abishai, one of David's men
Achish, King of Gath
The Commander of the Philistine Army
Eli, Amasa, Abiathar, Joab, and others
  of David's men
An Amalekite
A Young Man

SCENE ONE

At Gibeah. Saul and a few of his close advisors are gathered in the center of the army encampment talking, when a man from Ziph enters.

Saul: You have come from Ziph with some word you want to give me?

Ziphite: Yes, King Saul. I have come to tell you that David is hiding in our territory. He has many men with him. I was told that you would like to have this information.

Saul: Yes. Thank you for coming to me. You shall be rewarded with gifts. (*Turns to one of his men.*) See that this man is properly rewarded and taken care of until he leaves for his own country.

The Ziphite and servant leave.

Saul: I'm going to find that David and kill him. We won't lose any time about it either. Break up camp here and prepare to leave for Ziph.

41

ABNER: But this is a dangerous thing to do. David has many men.

AHIJAH: Yes. Not only did all his family go into hiding when he left our camp, but now I understand that a great many others have joined his band of outlaws. He has a whole army of his own!

SAUL: I know all that. But what an army it is! Everyone who's running away from his debts or from anything else joins David!

ABNER: But there are about four hundred men, I hear. Even if they are a lawless and disreputable lot, that still is quite an army!

AHIJAH: And that isn't all. He can count on allies. He's a clever man, that David. In one way or another, he's made bargains with no telling how many cities and tribes. He promises protection here, threatens a raid there, and so on till he has everybody right where he wants him. I say he's a clever man—and a dangerous one.

SAUL (*his temper rising*): That's just it! He's a dangerous man. I said I was going to kill him, and I intend to do so. We shall depart for Ziph!

SCENE TWO

The wilderness of Ziph in the middle of the night. David and Abishai are approaching Saul's camp.

DAVID: They can't be far from here. The spies I sent out reported that Saul's camp was on the hill right near those rocks. And this is just about where we saw the tents as we looked down from the hill opposite.

ABISHAI: Yes, I believe it is. Oh, there, I think I see the outline of the tents now. How will we find Saul?

DAVID: His tent will be right in the middle.

ABISHAI: Surely someone will hear us if we have to go into the center of the encampment!

DAVID: Not if we're very careful. His men have been marching through these hills all day. They'll be too tired to wake easily.

The two men creep quietly through the camp until they come to the tent in the center. They step inside and watch the king for a moment

as he sleeps, his spear stuck in the ground near his head and a jar of water nearby. Abner is asleep beside the king.

ABISHAI (*whispering*):   Well, there's your enemy. God has given him to you. Let me take his spear and pin him to the ground.

DAVID: No, do not kill him. The Lord has made him king of Israel. It would be a great wrong for me to kill him. But take his spear and that jar of water beside it, and let us go.

Abishai takes the spear, and holding it in his hand, he looks again at the king and then at David. He cannot understand why David does not take advantage of this moment and kill Saul. Since it is obvious that David is not going to change his mind, Abishai picks up the jar of water. The two men creep out of the camp and climb the hill that is opposite.

DAVID (*in a very loud voice*):   Abner, Abner, the son of Ner, answer me!

ABNER (*waking up with a start and looking around, as if very much confused*):   Who are you?

DAVID: Abner, why haven't you kept watch over the king? Someone came to destroy him, and you did not even know it. You deserve to die for failing to protect the king.

Abner by this time has come out of the tent, but he is still in a daze. Saul also comes out and listens to David's voice.

DAVID: Look, Abner. See where the king's spear is! And see the jar of water that was by his head!

SAUL: David, David, is that your voice?

DAVID: Yes, O king, it is my voice. Why are you pursuing me, Saul? What have I done that you want to kill me?

SAUL: It is I who have done wrong, David, my son. I will not harm you. I have been foolish to pursue you as I have. You have shown your loyalty to me. You could have taken my life, and you did not.

DAVID: Here is your spear, Saul. Send a boy over to get it. I had my chance to kill you today; the Lord gave it to me. But I could not kill you, because the Lord has made you king. As I saved your life, so may God save me from harm and trouble.

SAUL: The Lord bless you, David, my son. You will do great things.

SCENE THREE

Many months later. David is still an outlaw. Now the Philistine armies are gathering to attack Israel. Achish of Gath who has had many dealings with David, and who has brought David and his forces to join the Philistine army, talks with the commander.

COMMANDER OF THE PHILISTINES (*to Achish*): What are those Hebrews doing back there at the rear of the line? We're going to fight with the Israelites. How is it that there are some among us?

ACHISH: That's David back there. He has been with me for many months.

COMMANDER OF THE PHILISTINES: What has he been doing with you? I know he had to flee from King Saul, but how do you happen to have anything to do with him?

ACHISH: He came to live here in the land of the Philistines at Gath. He was faithful to every agreement he made with me. When he made raids on the cities around, he always gave me my share of the spoils. After a time I gave him a town on the border, where he and all his family and his followers now live. He has made such enemies of his own people that he will be our servant always.

COMMANDER OF THE PHILISTINES: I don't know about that. I doubt that he can be trusted to go against his fellow Israelites.

ACHISH: But when I asked David to come he said, "You know what I can do." Come to think of it, though, that wasn't a very definite promise to fight!

COMMANDER OF THE PHILISTINES: David and his men should not be with us. They might easily turn against us when the battle with their countrymen begins. Send them back.

ACHISH: If you insist, I'll go tell David, but I think you're wrong. I have never found any fault with him or had any trouble with him. (*He walks to the back of the line-up of warriors.*)

ACHISH (*to David*): It seems to me that you should be allowed to go with us in the campaign against Israel. You've been loyal to me, and you've kept your word in all our dealings. But the commander of the army does not approve. You'll have to go back. I hope you'll go without making any trouble.

DAVID: Have I done something to displease you? Have I ever done anything wrong in all this time I've served you?

ACHISH: No, you've done no wrong. It's the commander of the army who has said that you cannot go into battle with us. Early tomorrow morning you must leave us and go back to the place I have given you. (*Exits.*)

DAVID (*to himself*): Well, that takes care of that problem. I didn't want to join the Philistines to fight against King Saul, but there was no way to get out of my agreement with Achish. Now I can go back to my family in peace.

SCENE FOUR

A few days later in the town of Ziklag which was given to David by Achish. The men are just arriving as the scene opens.

DAVID (*entering the town and seeing that it is deserted*): What has happened? Where is everyone?

THE MEN WITH DAVID: Everyone is gone! Look at the damage; everything has been burned!

DAVID: All our women have been carried off! Who could have done this terrible thing?

There is great wailing among all the men.

ELI: We never should have left here. Some enemies must have known that all the men were away.

AMASA: We should have stayed right here instead of going off with the Philistines.

46

ELI: It was David's doing that we went off!

CHORUS: It's David's fault. Stone him!

DAVID: Be quiet! I shall ask the Lord what we should do now.

David goes off. The men continue to weep and angrily to protest what has happened. David returns after a few minutes.

ABISHAI: What does the Lord say?

DAVID: That we should pursue the men who have done this. We shall be able to overtake them if we leave immediately.

SCENE FIVE

Several hours later. The men in pursuit of the raiders stop by a brook in the open country.

ELI: I can't go on. I'm too exhausted to move from this spot. (*Almost falls beside the brook.*)

ABIATHAR (*sinking down beside Eli*): Nor can I go another step.

DAVID: But we must go on. There'll be no chance of overtaking the men who raided our town if we do not keep going.

ELI: But I can't go on.

DAVID: All the men who are too tired to continue will stay here with our baggage and equipment. The rest will go on.

A number of men settle down by the brook, but a larger number start off with David to continue the journey.

SCENE SIX

The same place two days later. David and the men who went with him return to the brook, bringing their wives and children, all the possessions that had been taken from their city, and much more. The men who stayed at the brook run out to meet the approaching caravan.

ELI (*to David*): You found them! Praise the Lord!

DAVID: Yes, we found the Amalekites who raided our city. They were eating and drinking and dancing when we came upon them. We wiped them out and recovered our families and possessions, and we took much more also.

ABISHAI (*who has been with David*): Yes, look at the spoil! We did well!

JOAB: These men who did not go with us—we don't have to give them any of the spoil. Each of them can have his own wife and children, but that is all!

AMASA: That's right. The spoil belongs to us—to those who fought for it.

DAVID: No, my brothers. What the Lord has given to us belongs to all. Those who stay by the baggage and those who go down to the battle must share alike. This will be the law among us.

SCENE SEVEN

Some days later, in the town of Ziklag. An Amalekite enters and seeks for David. When he finds him he kneels down before him.

DAVID: Where do you come from?

AMALEKITE: I have come from the Israelite camp. I escaped from there.

DAVID: What has happened? How did the battle go?

AMALEKITE: Many, many people are dead. King Saul and his son Jonathan are dead.

DAVID: How do you know this?

AMALEKITE: I was right there. King Saul was wounded. He was leaning on his spear, and the enemy was close around him. He called to me and asked me to slay him. He was in great pain, and he feared that he would be taken by the Philistines. So I killed him.

DAVID (*tearing his clothes and weeping*): Saul and Jonathan! O ye daughters of Israel, weep over Saul! Weep over Jonathan!

There is much wailing among the people. Then after a time David turns again to the Amalekite.

48

DAVID: How could you kill King Saul—the king of Israel, the man whom God himself made king? You, there (*pointing to a young man*)—come here and kill this man who has slain the king. (*To the Amalekite*) You yourself told us you killed King Saul. Your blood is upon your own head.

The young man steps up and kills the Amalekite. David and the others go on weeping over Saul and Jonathan.

DAVID: Saul and Jonathan, beloved and lovely!
    In life and death they were not divided;
  they were swifter than eagles,
    they were stronger than lions.
  Ye daughters of Israel, weep over Saul,
    weep over Jonathan.

SCENE EIGHT

The city of Hebron, some days later. David and his wives and all his men march into the city.

CHORUS OF MEN WITH DAVID: Hail, the king! Hail, David who will reign in Hebron!

DAVID: We will make this city of Hebron our capital, for the Lord has told us to come here. We have much work to do, for all the people of Israel must know that I am king.

There is a chorus of "Yes" and "Hail, the king."

DAVID: Now, my first act as king will be this: We will send word to the men who buried Saul—the men of Jabeshgilead. Here (*motioning several of his messengers to him*), take this word to the men who buried Saul. Say to them, "May the Lord bless you, for you showed your loyalty to your king by giving him a proper burial. I will do good to you for your faithfulness and loyalty. Be strong and courageous, for your king is dead. Now I am the king!"

PEOPLE: David is king! Soon all Israel will know that David is king!

1 Samuel 22:1–2; 26:1—28:2; 29:1—30:25; 2 Samuel 1:1—2:7. David's lament at the end of Scene Seven is from 2 Samuel 1:23–24.

A Man Who Dared to Challenge a King

AHAB was king of Israel. His wife, Jezebel, was a princess from Tyre who did not care anything about the God of the Hebrew people. Elijah was a prophet of Ahab's day who often spoke out against the king and Jezebel.

CHARACTERS: NABOTH
                  AHAB, king of Israel
                  JEZEBEL, wife of Ahab
                  MESSENGER
                  ELIJAH, the prophet

SCENE ONE

The vineyard of Naboth, which is next to the palace of King Ahab in the city of Jezreel. Naboth is standing in the vineyard as Ahab walks toward him from the palace gardens.

NABOTH (*bowing toward the king*): Ahab, the king!

AHAB: Naboth, my friend and neighbor! Do you have a few minutes to talk with me?

NABOTH: Surely. Will you join me here on this bench?

Ahab and Naboth sit down.

AHAB: Naboth, your vineyard is beautiful. It must be a great joy to you.

NABOTH: It is! It is! Not only the fruits of the vineyard but the sky, the sunsets, the smell of the plants and the fruits—everything is a great delight to me.

AHAB (*slowly*): Yes, I suppose so.

51

NABOTH: This vineyard has belonged to my family for many years. My fathers and my father's fathers for many generations have stood on this very plot of ground and have loved it as I do. And my children who come after me will also love it and care for it.

AHAB (*uneasily*): Naboth, I will come to the point. I want your vineyard.

NABOTH (*surprised*): You what?

AHAB: I must have your vineyard!

NABOTH: But I cannot . . .

AHAB: I must have your vineyard. I need more land next to the palace for a vegetable garden. Your vineyard is the ideal spot.

NABOTH: But I . . . but this land belongs to my family!

AHAB: Naboth, do not make me angry. I will give you another vineyard *much* better than this one. Or if you wish, I will give you money far in excess of what your vineyard is worth. Which will it be?

NABOTH (*firmly*): I am sorry, my king. This land has been in my family for many generations. You know the customs of our land. The vineyard does not belong only to me. It belongs to my fathers who lived here before me and to my children and to their children who will come after me. I cannot give it to you.

Ahab rises from the bench, obviously upset. He walks across the vineyard, onto the palace grounds, and into the palace.

SCENE TWO

Ahab's bedroom in the palace a short time later. Ahab is in his bed, his face turned toward the wall. Jezebel enters the room.

JEZEBEL (*concerned*): Ahab, why do you lie there like that? I'm told that you refuse to eat. What's the matter with you? Are you sick?

AHAB (*face still to the wall*): No.

JEZEBEL: Whatever is the matter?

AHAB: Nothing.

JEZEBEL: Ahab, don't be so difficult. What has happened?

AHAB (*slowly turning toward Jezebel*): I have talked with Naboth, and he refuses to trade or to sell his vineyard.

JEZEBEL: Is that all that's the matter? Here I thought you were sick or something.

AHAB: But I want that land!

JEZEBEL: Ahab, you amaze me. Are you not the king of all Israel? Take the land!

AHAB: But I cannot. Naboth is within his rights to refuse to give it up.

JEZEBEL: Of all things! Of course you can take the land! Aren't you the king of Israel? If you aren't able to seize an insignificant vineyard from a farmer, I will do it myself! Now get up off your bed; eat and be cheerful. I will take care of the vineyard.

Scene Three

An hour later in Jezebel's apartment in the palace. A messenger for whom she has sent enters the room.

JEZEBEL: Here is a letter to the leaders of the city of Jezreel. Be sure they understand that it is from the king.

MESSENGER: I will do as you say.

JEZEBEL: The letter arranges for witnesses to declare that Naboth of Jezreel has cursed God and the king and must therefore be put to death.

MESSENGER: I will see that all the king's orders are obeyed. (*He bows and leaves.*)

Scene Four

Three days later in Ahab's throne room. He is at work on official papers as Jezebel enters.

JEZEBEL: The deed is done!

AHAB: What deed?

JEZEBEL: Naboth is dead. The leaders of the city have just sent a messenger saying that he was stoned to death this morning just outside the city. He was charged with cursing God and the king.

AHAB: But he did not curse God and me, did he?

JEZEBEL: Of course not, but I arranged for witnesses to say that he did. Now quickly, go and seize the vineyard.

AHAB: I will go.

SCENE FIVE

A few minutes later in the vineyard. As Ahab enters, the prophet Elijah appears before him.

AHAB: Have you found me, O my enemy?

ELIJAH: I have found you. What you have done is evil in the sight of the Lord. You have killed Naboth—you and your wife Jezebel—and you have come to take possession of land that does not belong to you.

AHAB (*tearing his robes*): I have sinned against the Lord.

ELIJAH: The Lord says, "I will bring evil upon you; I will sweep you away because of your sin. And, as for Jezebel, the dogs shall eat her."

AHAB (*continuing to tear his kingly robes*): I repent of the wrong I have done to Naboth. For the rest of my days I will go around in sackcloth instead of these robes. I will fast; I will be humble before the Lord, and obedient.

1 Kings 21

"Let Justice Roll Down Like Waters"

AMOS was growing more furious every minute. He had come to Bethel the day before to sell some of his sheep, because he had heard that prices were a little better in the north. But now he wished he had stayed in Judah. He had been cheated in the marketplace. "These sheep are much too skinny," the dealer had said, "and the wool is a poor quality." Amos knew better, but no matter how much he argued he could not get a fair price from the sheep dealer.

Being cheated was only the beginning. Nowhere had he seen people so cruelly mistreated as here in Israel! How could God's people act this way?

"I'm only a shepherd," he thought. "I have no business deciding what is right or wrong. But what else can I do? I know that our God demands justice and mercy. And I have eyes in my head—I can see what is going on."

As Amos stood in the marketplace, lost in thought, a small boy darted out from between two stalls. Because the child was looking back over his shoulder, he could not see where he was going and ran right into Amos.

"Whoa there," said the shepherd, catching the boy by the shoulders. "Where are you going in such a hurry?"

The boy twisted away, but not before Amos saw that he was crying.

"Here, lad, what's the matter?"

The boy sniffed loudly and rubbed one dusty, bare foot against the other. "They—they took my brother," he stammered. "And—and they were going to take me, too, but I ran away!"

"They took your brother?" Amos was puzzled. "Who are 'they'—and where did they take him?"

"The man who lends money—my mother couldn't pay him—and he took Joel and s-sold him!" The boy was sobbing so loudly that Amos could

55

hardly understand him. But suddenly the crying stopped, and the boy looked up at the big shepherd with terror in his eyes. "Are you one of them? You'll take me back—you'll sell *me* too!" Before Amos could move, the boy tore off down the narrow street and disappeared in the crowd.

Amos remained standing where he was, looking after the boy. "He couldn't have been more than seven," he thought. "Seven years old—sold as a slave!" Angrily he turned and strode back the way he had come. Something had to be done, but what? What could one man do in the face of so much evil?

Now Amos was coming to the gate where the judges sat to decide cases of justice. "Justice!" he muttered to himself. "How can justice be done by wicked men?" He was remembering what he had seen the day before as he passed this very gate. He had noticed a merchant, wrapped in an embroidered silk cloak and reeking of costly ointment, talking with one of the judges. The rich man slipped his hand under his cloak, drew out a small leather bag, and handed it to the judge. Amos understood at once what was going on. The man was offering a bribe!

The shepherd stayed nearby to see what would happen next. Very shortly another man joined the other two—plainly a poor man by his clothing—and began to speak with the judge. When he finished, Amos heard the judge say, "No, I cannot decide in your favor. Your landlord is in the right. You must pay him the full amount of grain by next week, or a fine will be necessary. Yes, I think a fine of seven skins of new wine— and as a pledge that you can be trusted, give him your cloak."

The poor man looked as if he would gladly have struck both men, but he silently removed his cloak and gave it to the landlord. The rich man winked at the judge as he folded the cloak carefully and tucked it under his arm. The poor man turned and walked slowly away. Amos knew very well that this man had no other cloak, and he also knew that the judge and the landlord were aware of this. The poor man would have to sleep without a cover, for his cloak served also as a blanket. Amos knew, too, that the man would never be able to pay the required amount of grain— or the fine, for that matter. This was wrong! It was not the way Israelites should treat one another. These people had forgotten God completely!

Amos continued his walk through the city, past dirty children playing in the street, past open doorways through which a few poor furnishings could be seen. Through one door he saw an old woman rocking a baby in her arms. The child was crying pitifully. In the courtyard two older children were playing, both so thin and pale that Amos wanted to weep.

Then suddenly, as he approached the temple area, the scene changed. The houses were larger, and several of them were decorated with ivory carvings around the doorways. Amos heard the people inside laughing, and from one house came the sound of a lyre and singing. He looked at the sun. It was not yet midday, and already these people were making merry!

Amos' anger grew within him. He wanted to fling something at the walls of these fine houses, to spit at their owners. There was so much poverty in Israel, and these wealthy people did not even care!

As he passed an especially large house, Amos heard a woman's voice screech out in anger, "Why have you come home at this hour, you lazy wretch! Go back to the market! How can you make any money this way? I must have a new dress for the feast, and we are nearly out of wine! Get out of here—what kind of husband *are* you?"

Amos was disgusted. Such a woman would come to a sorry end. Amos could picture her dead body being hoisted right out of the street by a huge fishhook.

At last he reached the temple. But even here he found only disappointment. The priests were offering the daily sacrifices as the law required. People stood in line to present their tithes. Amos heard singing—songs of praise to God. He smiled bitterly. The whole scene seemed like a play. All these people were pretending to be so religious, acting out the part of faithful Israelites. How could they go through the motions so seriously when only minutes before they had been lying, cheating, and stealing?

Surely God would laugh at their sacrifices and turn away from their songs. Amos took a last look at this sanctuary of the Lord and walked sadly down the steps. He wanted only to go home, back to Tekoa and his flocks. He could see no hope for these people, for surely God would not stand for their actions. "God demands that his people live in justice and mercy, because he is just and merciful," thought Amos. "But there is no justice or mercy in Israel. Instead of trusting in the Lord, the people have put their trust in riches. They trample the poor in the dust. They feast and celebrate at the expense of their starving brothers. And their worship is like play-acting, because their actions say that their sacrifices don't mean anything."

Amos could foresee only destruction for Israel. How could such a corrupt nation stand if an enemy were to sweep down upon her? The people were not united. They would never be able to defend themselves. In his mind's eye, Amos saw the wealth of Israel being carried away by an invading army, the temple destroyed, the people starving. No one could escape the anger of the Lord! When they no longer knew God's presence, the people would realize that their worship had been only play-acting.

Israel must be warned that disaster was not far away. Israel must be warned to repent, to turn back to *true* worship. "Let justice roll down like waters," thought Amos, "and righteousness like an ever-flowing stream. Then the Israelites will be true people of God again."

Amos stopped in the middle of the street. Perhaps Israel could yet be saved. He did not feel much hope for this, but perhaps . . .

"I am only a shepherd," he thought, shaking his head. "Surely the Lord doesn't expect *me* to speak his word to the people. Who would listen to me?" He walked on a few steps and then suddenly turned and started back toward the temple. "Yes, I must speak! God has called me to warn the people."

"Justice," he said aloud, "like waters pouring down to purify my people." And he retraced his steps to the temple, convinced that somehow the Lord would speak through him.

The book of Amos. Amos' words "Let justice roll down like waters . . ." are from 5:24.

The King Who Wanted to Obey God

AFTER David and his son Solomon died, the kingdom of Israel was split in two. The northern part was called Israel and the southern part called Judah. Many years after the split, Israel was destroyed by Assyria. Then only the southern kingdom, Judah, remained. This play takes place in Judah, nearly a hundred years after Assyria had conquered Israel.

CHARACTERS: JOSIAH, king of Judah
    NATHANIEL, a friend of the young king
    HILKIAH, the high priest in the temple at Jerusalem
    SHAPHAN, the king's secretary
    JOAH, the recorder
    THREE LEVITES

SCENE ONE

The city of Jerusalem. Josiah and Nathaniel are playing in the courtyard of the palace. Josiah is eight years old and has just been made king of Judah after the murder of his father.

NATHANIEL: I'll be the king, Josiah, and you be the prophet. We'll have a fight—you know, the way they always do. And I can put you in prison.

JOSIAH: But I really *am* the king, Nathaniel.

NATHANIEL: I know, but we're just pretending. I'll pretend I'm your grandfather. Then you'll have a harder time. You know what he did to the prophets! (*He slashes his throat with a forefinger.*) Whack! Off with your head! (*Pauses.*) Say, Josiah, why did your grandfather kill so many people? Just because he was king?

59

JOSIAH: I don't know. I never thought about it before. I guess they did bad things. (*Pauses.*) I don't think I'll kill people. Hilkiah says it's wrong to kill. He says God doesn't want us to hurt other people.

NATHANIEL: Which god?

JOSIAH: *God*—the Lord, stupid. What other God is there?

NATHANIEL: What do you mean, what other God is there? There are lots of gods. We worship lots of them. You have to, or things won't go right. They'll get angry if you don't give them sacrifices.

JOSIAH: Hilkiah says the Lord is the only one we should worship.

NATHANIEL: But he isn't the only God.

JOSIAH: Prove it!

NATHANIEL: All right! Come on over to the temple and I *will* prove it!

The boys run down the street to the temple.

NATHANIEL (*stopping in the courtyard*): See—there's an altar to one of them.

JOSIAH: That's the Lord's altar. Don't you know anything?

NATHANIEL (*looks angrily at Josiah*): Well, come on inside and I'll show you some more. (*He runs up the steps to the porch.*) See? Now do you believe me? (*Points to altars in the porch.*) All the heavenly host— the sun, the moon, the stars—they all have altars. And the goddess Asherah has an altar in the holy place even.

JOSIAH (*earnestly*): Yes, but Nathaniel, those idols aren't really gods. Hilkiah says they're false gods and that we must worship only the Lord. He's the only one who can *do* anything.

NATHANIEL: No, he isn't! Why, your own grandfather worshiped these gods—and he made all our people worship them too. And it worked, didn't it? I mean Assyria didn't destroy us. The people prayed to the Assyrian gods, and the gods protected them. Your grandfather sacrificed his own son to them—don't you remember?

JOSIAH: I know he did, but it was wrong. Hilkiah says the Lord doesn't want human sacrifice.

NATHANIEL (*angrily*): You just don't *listen*! I told you the Lord isn't the only God!

JOSIAH: Don't you want to play king and prophet, Nathaniel?

NATHANIEL: No! I'm going home. If you're not going to pay any attention to what I tell you, I'm not going to play with you.

SCENE TWO

A few minutes later. Josiah is sitting on the temple steps. Hilkiah the priest comes out of the temple and nearly trips over the boy.

HILKIAH: Well, my son, what are you doing here alone? Does anyone at the palace know where you are?

JOSIAH (*looking at the ground*): No.

HILKIAH: What's the matter, Josiah?

JOSIAH: Oh, nothing. Nathaniel and I were playing, and he got mad and went home. He's so stubborn!

HILKIAH: What happened?

JOSIAH: I said that the Lord is the only God we are supposed to worship— you told me that—and he said there were lots of gods. So we had a fight, sort of. Hilkiah, why does everyone but us worship lots of gods?

HILKIAH: We are Israelites, Josiah. This means that we believe that our God brought us out of Egypt many years ago and gave us this land. He also commanded us to worship only him, and our forefathers promised to do that. Because he has been so good to us, we ought to obey him and live as he wants us to live. But we have had much trouble with our enemies in these last years. Assyria conquered the northern kingdom of Israel and carried off many of the people as captives.

Josiah nods.

HILKIAH: Our kings—the kings of Judah—were afraid that the same thing would happen to us, so they made treaties with the kings of Assyria.

Your grandfather, Manasseh, did this. He promised to be loyal to Assyria, and this meant he had to worship their gods. But he went much further than he needed to. He brought in many other gods besides those of the Assyrians, and supported people who practiced magic, fortune-telling, and all sorts of evil.

JOSIAH: But the Assyrian gods and those others—they aren't really gods, are they?

HILKIAH: No, they are not real gods, Josiah. And we need not fear the strength of Assyria any longer. So now we must get rid of these foreign gods and all the evil things that go with them. We must remind the people that we have only one God. Otherwise, we will see God's punishment here in Judah as surely as Israel was punished. I remember what a prophet of God said while Manasseh was alive: "I will wipe Jerusalem as one wipes a dish, wiping it and turning it upside down."

JOSIAH (*shivering*): I'm not sure I want to be king, Hilkiah.

HILKIAH: You will be a good king, my son. The Lord is with you. You will do great things for him.

SCENE THREE

The temple in Jerusalem. Josiah is talking to Hilkiah the priest. Josiah has been reigning in Judah for eighteen years. He has spent the last six years supervising the destruction of foreign idols and their altars in Judah and in what used to be the northern kingdom of Israel.

JOSIAH: I don't understand it, Hilkiah. (*Smiles.*) We just get one job done and ten more appear out of nowhere!

HILKIAH: What is it now? I thought everything was finished when you came back to Jerusalem last month. All the foreign gods and their altars have been destroyed. What remains to be done?

JOSIAH: Two things right now. First of all we have to find a place for all the country priests, the Levites, who are pouring into Jerusalem. That's *your* fault, Hilkiah. (*Laughs.*) If you hadn't insisted that Jerusalem is the only proper place for sacrifices to the Lord, the Levites would still be taking care of the village altars. But now they have no jobs. What are we going to do with them?

HILKIAH: Oh, don't worry about the Levites, Josiah. They are good workers; we can use them in the temple. But don't be so quick to place all the responsibility for that decision on my shoulders. After all, having the people come to Jerusalem for the feast days instead of celebrating them in their villages *will* help to unite the kingdom. And that was your idea, remember?

JOSIAH: I know, and I still think it was a good one. But I nearly forgot the second problem. We must do something about the temple. It's almost falling apart. It's been neglected for so long that it will take a great deal of stone and lumber even to make a beginning. The only trouble is that there isn't enough money in the treasury to make all the repairs that are needed. What are we going to do, Hilkiah?

HILKIAH: I don't think that's such an impossible problem, my son. As a matter of fact, that would be a good job for the Levites. Why not send some of them out to collect money from the people? Everyone used to contribute money for the upkeep of the village sanctuaries. Now these no longer exist, so the people can just as well give their offerings for the repair of the temple.

JOSIAH: That's a wonderful idea, Hilkiah! And the Levites can supervise the repair work, too, once the money has been collected. I'll speak to Shaphan, my secretary. He can get the project under way. (*Exits.*)

HILKIAH (*looking around*): At last the house of the Lord will be fit for his worship! How long I have waited for this day! The Lord has given us a wise and faithful king. Blessed be the name of the Lord!

SCENE FOUR

Six months later in the temple. Shaphan and Joah the recorder are speaking with Hilkiah.

SHAPHAN: And the king has instructed us to give the overseers this money that the Levites have collected from all Judah.

63

HILKIAH: Good. Have your men bring in the money while I find the Levites who are in charge. (*Exits.*)

Shaphan goes to the door and calls. Three men enter carrying leather bags. The men give the bags to Shaphan and leave again.

SHAPHAN (*looking around*): What a lot of work there is to be done! It will take many months.

JOAH: Yes, but we can be thankful for a king who cares about the temple. Josiah has done more for our nation than any king since David.

SHAPHAN: Well, he has certainly cleared out all the foreign gods. I wonder, though, whether the people really understand what is going on. They have worshiped so many gods for so long that I'm not sure they remember what kind of God the Lord is.

JOAH: You're right, Shaphan. The people need . . .

Hilkiah runs in, breathless, waving a scroll.

HILKIAH: Shaphan! Joah! I have found—look what I have found! The book of the law!

JOAH: What book of the law, Hilkiah?

HILKIAH: The law of the Lord, given through Moses! One of the Levites discovered it among the rubble in the women's court. It must have been here for years, and we didn't even know about it!

SHAPHAN: May I see it? (*Hilkiah hands him the scroll and he reads.*) I think the king should see this, Hilkiah. (*Turns scroll to the end and continues to read.*) This is frightening—column after column of curses—"if you forsake the Lord," it says. I'm almost afraid to show this to the king, Hilkiah. He takes these matters so seriously there's no telling what he might do.

HILKIAH: I should hope he would take this seriously, Shaphan! This law has been broken. Our people have served false gods, and I don't think even Josiah can force them to repent, although he has certainly tried. Now come, we must take this book to the king.

Scene Five

A little later, in the palace. Shaphan comes before Josiah with the scroll.

JOSIAH: You have returned so soon, Shaphan? Did you deliver my message to Hilkiah?

SHAPHAN: Yes, my lord. The money has been given to the overseers. (*He clears his throat.*) My lord, Hilkiah the priest has given me a book.

JOSIAH: A book? What kind of book?

SHAPHAN: This book, my lord. (*He holds out the scroll.*)

JOSIAH (*impatiently*): Well, what is it? Read it to me.

SHAPHAN (*clearing his throat again*): It's pretty long, my lord.

JOSIAH (*sternly*): Read the book, Shaphan.

SHAPHAN: Very well, my lord. (*He opens the scroll to the beginning and reads.*) "These are the laws which you shall obey in the land which the Lord has given you. You shall destroy all the places where the people who were here before you served their gods. . . ."

Scene Six

An hour later, in another room in the palace, where Hilkiah has been waiting. Shaphan bursts into the room.

SHAPHAN: Hilkiah! The king wants to see you!

HILKIAH: What? What's wrong, Shaphan?

SHAPHAN: The king is nearly out of his mind! I read the book to him, and when I got to the part about the curses for disobedience he began to tear his clothes with grief. Go quickly! I must find my son and two servants, and then I will join you. (*Exits.*)

Hilkiah enters the room where Josiah is pacing up and down, his clothes torn. He looks up as Hilkiah enters.

JOSIAH: We are doomed, Hilkiah! You have read the book you found in the temple?

HILKIAH: Yes, Josiah. I have read every word. (*He shakes his head sadly.*)

JOSIAH (*waving his arms*):   What are we going to do? Our fathers did not obey these laws. They went chasing after foreign gods. Many of our people still do not realize what it means to serve the Lord. What will happen to us, Hilkiah? Surely we will be punished!

Shaphan enters with three other men.

JOSIAH: Ah, Shaphan. I want you to go and inquire of the Lord for me, and for all Judah, concerning the words of this book. The Lord is certainly angry with us, because we have disobeyed the laws written here.

SHAPHAN: Yes, my lord. We will go at once to Huldah, the prophetess.

SCENE SEVEN

Later the same day. Shaphan and Hilkiah are reporting to Josiah.

SHAPHAN: Huldah said that the Lord will bring evil upon Judah because the people have forsaken him and worshiped other gods.

JOSIAH: There is no hope?

HILKIAH: No, Josiah. Judah will be destroyed. But it will not happen while you are alive. The Lord has seen your grief and your repentance, and he will show mercy upon you. You will not see the evil he is bringing upon this place.

JOSIAH: Blessed be the Lord! He has spared us in this generation. We must tell the people. Spread the word, Shaphan. Bring all the elders of Judah to Jerusalem. They must hear what is in this book. And we will make a promise to follow the Lord and keep all his commandments as they are written in this book. Our people will worship the Lord, and him only.

2 Chronicles 33—35. The words quoted by Hilkiah on page 62 are from 2 Kings 21:13. The book found in the temple was probably what is now Deuteronomy 12—28.

Thus Says the Lord

THE WORD of the Lord came to the prophet Jeremiah. "Go to the temple and tell all those who come to worship that they must change their ways. Warn them that I will not put up with their wrongdoing."

Jeremiah obeyed. For some years now he had been speaking God's word in and around Jerusalem. He was a faithful prophet but not an eager one. Often he complained to God and wished that the Lord had not called him to be one of his spokesmen.

This time Jeremiah went straight to the temple and stood in the court-yard where he could speak to the crowds that came through the gate on their way to worship. "Hear the word of the Lord," he began. As he spoke the people gathered around him.

"Change your ways; obey the Lord," Jeremiah went on. "Don't think that because you come to the temple you are safe, that you will always have this good land God has given you. The Lord says, 'I will let you live in this good land that I gave to your fathers of old, but only if you do justice to one another, only if you stop oppressing the poor, the widows, and the foreigners who live among you. I will let you live here only if you stop worshiping other gods and worship only the God who brought you out of Egypt and gave you this land.'"

Seeing the crowd around Jeremiah, some of the temple priests and prophets began to listen. These were dangerous words that the prophet was speaking! The priests knew that Jeremiah had approved of the reforms Josiah had made, but now he was saying that temple worship was not the most important way to serve God. He was prophesying against the temple, against the city!

"You shall die!" shouted one of the priests. Then speaking to the people, the priest said, "This man should be sentenced to death for what he is saying against this city."

Jeremiah answered, "God sent me here to say these things. Obey God and he will repent of his anger. As for me, I am in your hands. Do whatever seems right to you. But remember this: If you kill me, you will be bringing innocent blood upon yourselves, because God told me to say these things."

Some government officials, who had by this time joined the crowd, spoke up. "Jeremiah does not deserve to die. He has spoken in the Lord's name. We will bring evil on ourselves if we put him to death."

Other officials and elders agreed, and Jeremiah was released. But he was told not to preach in the temple courts again.

Before many days had passed, the word of the Lord came to Jeremiah again. "Go and prophesy so that all Jerusalem will hear." So Jeremiah preached in the streets and at the gates, wherever the people gathered. "Hear the word of the Lord," Jeremiah's voice would ring out. " 'Return, faithless Israel, and I will be merciful,' says the Lord. 'Return to me, amend your ways so that you may be saved from destruction.' "

Many people listened to Jeremiah, but few took him seriously, and even fewer tried to follow his words. But although his preaching had little effect on his listeners, the temple authorities believed he was a dangerous man. They were alarmed by his predictions that destruction would come upon the land. Some of Jeremiah's own relatives, urged on by the temple priests, insisted that he stop prophesying or be killed.

Jeremiah was bitter. The people did not heed his preaching, and now even his own relatives were plotting against him. "I know you are righteous, O God," Jeremiah cried, "but why is it that wicked people prosper? Why do you let them go on living? Your ways are puzzling to me. Why don't you take these evil ones, those who have plotted against me, and put them out like sheep for slaughter?"

Instead of answering Jeremiah's questions, God said, "There is work to be done, Jeremiah. There is harder work ahead than anything you have yet had to do. If you have raced with men on foot and they have made you so tired and full of complaints, how can you possibly race with horses?"

So Jeremiah stopped his complaining and went back to preaching. His message became more and more urgent. The armies from Babylon were conquering nation after nation. God would use these armies to bring destruction upon Jerusalem. "See, God's anger is kindled against us," Jeremiah warned. "Change your ways. Be faithful to God who brought us out of Egypt and gave us this good land. Stop worshiping other gods; do justice; be God's righteous, faithful people."

But the people still did not heed Jeremiah's words. He was ready to give up. "Why don't they listen to me?" he asked. "Is there no way to show them how great the danger is?"

Again the word of the Lord came to Jeremiah. "Don't give up. Go and buy a pottery flask. Then gather the people together and, in their presence, break the flask into little pieces. Say to them that their city will be broken in the same way if they do not hear my words."

Jeremiah went to the potter's shop and purchased a fine, large flask. Then he called together the city elders, the priests, and many others and took them to one of the city gates.

"Thus says the Lord," Jeremiah began. "Evil will come upon this place because the people have forsaken their God. The city will be destroyed and the people will fall by the sword of their enemies! You have brought this evil upon yourselves," Jeremiah went on. "You have refused to hear the word of the Lord and obey it."

Then holding up the beautiful, new flask where everyone could see it, Jeremiah said, "Because of your wrongdoing, the Lord will break this city as if it were a piece of pottery." As he spoke, Jeremiah hit the flask against the gate and broke it.

The people gasped. The handsome, new flask was in a thousand pieces! It could never be mended.

"Surely now these people understand," Jeremiah thought.

But if they did understand, not many of them took the message seriously. Some continued to worship other gods. Some went on as if faithfulness to God meant only offering sacrifices in the temple. Even the dramatic warning of the broken flask did not bring the people back to the righteousness and justice that God required of them.

Now Jeremiah was too discouraged to go on. No matter what he did, the people would not change. "Look at them, God," he complained. "They refuse to feel sorry for what they've done. They refuse to repent."

Jeremiah wished he'd never become a prophet. For years he had been preaching the word of the Lord, and what good had come of his labors? The people ignored him. They even made fun of him.

"I've been faithful to you, Lord," Jeremiah said. "Remember me. It's for your sake that I'm all alone, rejected by everybody. Your words have been a joy to me, and I have preached them, but the people curse me. Woe is me. I wish I'd never been born!"

God answered Jeremiah, "Return to me. Don't say worthless things like that! If you say what is worthwhile, you shall be as my own mouth, speaking to the people for me. I will strengthen you."

Jeremiah sighed. This happened every time he complained to God. The Lord listened to him, but then he sent him right back to the people, right back to preach the words that the people did not want to hear. "I decide that I'm through with being a prophet," Jeremiah said to himself, "and that I won't ever speak God's name any more, and right away I feel as if there were a fire in my bones. I cannot keep the fire inside. I have to speak out again."

So Jeremiah went back to his preaching. In the marketplace and at the gates of the city he prophesied—everywhere except in the temple courts where he was not allowed. But the word of the Lord needed to be spoken in the temple; Jeremiah knew this, but how was he to do it?

Then one day God said to him, "Write my message against the wrongdoing of Israel on a scroll. Then the scroll can be read in the temple even though you cannot go there."

Jeremiah called his secretary, Baruch, to him and told him that he must write down all the words he dictated. Then on a feast day when many people would be in the temple courts Baruch would read the scroll to them.

Carefully Baruch wrote all the words of the Lord that Jeremiah spoke. Then on the appointed day he went to the temple and began to read.

As soon as the temple leaders realized what was happening, they hurried off to the king's house and told the princes and government officials that Baruch was reading Jeremiah's prophecies in the temple courts. Immediately the princes told the priests to bring Baruch to them.

When the secretary arrived, they said, "Sit down and read." Baruch did as he was told.

"Did Jeremiah dictate these words?" one of the officials asked when Baruch had finished.

"Yes," the secretary answered. "He dictated them to me, and I wrote them with ink on the scroll."

"We must report this to the king," one of the officials said, taking the scroll from Baruch.

As Baruch started to leave, one of the men who was friendly toward Jeremiah drew him aside and said, "You and Jeremiah are in danger. Go and hide, both of you, and don't tell anyone where you are." Baruch thanked the man and hurried off.

When the officials told the king how Jeremiah had arranged for the word of the Lord to be read in the temple, he became furious. "Get the scroll and read it to me," he ordered.

Sitting before the fire warming his hands, the king listened as one of the princes read the first columns of the scroll.

"Give it to me," the king demanded when the reader paused for a moment. Slowly, as if he were greatly enjoying what he was doing, the king took his penknife and with a flourish sliced off the part of the scroll that had been read and threw it into the fire.

Some of the princes and officials who were present tried to stop him because they did not want to see Jeremiah's words destroyed. But the king would not listen to them. "Go on," he commanded the reader.

Once again the king listened and once again he took the scroll, cut off the part that had been read, and burned it. Over and over again he did this until the entire scroll had been read and burned. Then the king ordered three of the princes to find Baruch and Jeremiah and arrest them.

Meanwhile Baruch had returned to Jeremiah and reported what had happened. Heeding the warning of the government official, the two men went into hiding, and the princes could not find them.

Before long, Jeremiah heard through his friends that the king had destroyed the scroll. The prophet was greatly disturbed. Once again his work had come to nothing. The scroll that Baruch had written so carefully had been cut up and burned piece by piece! Not only that; the king was angry. Jeremiah's life was in danger. Why hadn't he long ago given up being a prophet of the Lord? Jeremiah wondered. What good had any of his work done? The whole land was in danger, and neither the king nor the people would listen.

"Look at these people," Jeremiah complained to the Lord, "and the king too. No one will listen."

But again the word of the Lord came to Jeremiah. "Take another scroll and write on it," the Lord said. "Write everything that was on the first scroll and more that I will tell you."

Jeremiah sighed. Once again he took a scroll and called Baruch to him.

As soon as his secretary was ready to write down his words, Jeremiah began, "Thus says the Lord, 'You have forsaken me. You have not obeyed my voice. Return, O faithless children. . . .'"

Jeremiah 7:1–7, 26; 11:20–12:6, 19; 15:10–19; 20:9, 36; 3:12–14

Great-Grandmother to King David

AT THE TIME the book of Ruth was written, the Jews in power were trying to purify their nation and their religion. They were especially opposed to Jews marrying foreigners. The author of the book of Ruth did not agree with this idea at all. To get his point across he used an old, old folktale about a very good woman, Naomi, and her faithful daughter-in-law, Ruth, who was from the land of Moab. After the author had finished telling the story, he made his point even more strongly. He said in Ruth 4:17–22 that Ruth, a foreigner, was the great-grandmother of David, the greatest king the people of Israel had ever had!

CHARACTERS: NAOMI
               RUTH
               ORPAH
               WOMEN OF BETHLEHEM
               REAPERS
               BOAZ
               SERVANT TO BOAZ
               KINSMAN
               ELDERS

SCENE ONE

The frontier of Moab. Ruth and Orpah have come this far with their mother-in-law, Naomi, who is returning to the city of Bethlehem after a number of years in Moab.

NAOMI: Farewell, my daughters. You have been good to me. And both of you were good wives to my two sons while they lived. I shall miss you, but it will be good to be in my own land once again, among my own people.

75

RUTH: We won't say farewell because we are coming with you, Naomi.

NAOMI: No, you must not. You must both return to your parents. You belong here in Moab among your own people. You will find husbands here and be happy. (*She kisses her two daughters-in-law.*)

ORPAH: No, we will go with you to Bethlehem.

NAOMI: Why do you want to come with me? If I had other sons, they would marry you according to our custom, and your sons would then carry on the name of your dead husbands. But I have no other sons. My husband is dead, and I am too old to marry again. I'm sorry for your sakes that your husbands are dead and that you have no brothers-in-law to take you as their wives. All that has happened is bitter to me.

ORPAH: Perhaps you are right. I will stay among my own people. (*She kisses her mother-in-law and exits.*)

NAOMI: Ruth, you, too, must remain among your own people here in Moab.

RUTH: Don't beg me to leave you. Wherever you go, I will go. Where you live, I will live. Your people will be my people, and your God my God. Where you die, I will die, and nothing but death will ever part us.

NAOMI (*moved by what Ruth has said*): I don't know what more I can say to persuade you. I can tell that your mind is made up. Your loyalty to me is too much, but I am grateful.

The two women exit together.

SCENE TWO

Several days later. Ruth and Naomi are entering Bethlehem. Some women at the well see them and recognize Naomi.

FIRST WOMAN: Naomi!

SECOND WOMAN: You've come back home!

THIRD WOMAN: I can't believe it! Is it really you?

NAOMI: Yes, but don't call me Naomi. Call me Mara instead, for these have been bitter years for me. I come back without husband or sons. And I have no grandchildren. It is a bitter thing to have no one to come after me, and no one to continue our name.

FIRST WOMAN: But at least you are among your own people—and we are glad to have you back.

The women exit, and Naomi and Ruth continue to walk toward Naomi's house.

NAOMI: Our life here will not be easy. We are very poor.

RUTH: But we'll manage in some way. Didn't you tell me that in Bethlehem the poor can follow the reapers in the fields and take whatever is left behind as the grain is harvested? That's what I'll do to get food for us.

NAOMI: But you are a foreigner and may not have the same rights as our own people. I'm afraid you may not be allowed to glean in the fields.

RUTH: Let me go anyway. Perhaps I will find favor in the sight of some landowner.

NAOMI: All right. It will do no harm to try.

SCENE THREE

In the fields belonging to Boaz. Some men are harvesting, and several women are binding up the grain in sheaves. Ruth follows along behind them gathering up the pieces that are left. Boaz enters.

BOAZ: The Lord be with you!

REAPERS: The Lord bless you!

BOAZ (*to the servant in charge*): Who is that woman over there gleaning? She is a stranger to me.

SERVANT: She is that Moabite woman who came to Bethlehem with Naomi. She's Naomi's daughter-in-law. She asked me if she could

gather the pieces of grain that were left after the harvest. She has been working since very early morning without resting.

Boaz walks over to Ruth.

Boaz: My daughter, you are welcome to glean in my fields. Don't go anywhere else. Stay close to the women who are binding the sheaves. There you will be safe. I will charge the men to let you alone. When you are thirsty you may drink the water the men have brought from the well.

Ruth: Why have I found favor in your eyes? You know that I am a foreigner.

BOAZ: I have heard about you and know what you have done for your mother-in-law. I have heard how you left your own father and mother and your own land to come with Naomi. I know that you have chosen to live among us and to be faithful to the God of Israel.

RUTH: You are very kind to me.

BOAZ: Come over here and eat some bread. You may dip it in this wine.

Ruth sits down. Boaz gives her more food than she can eat, and she puts some away for Naomi. Boaz walks over to his servant.

BOAZ: Let the Moabite woman glean wherever she wants. You may even pull some of the grain from the bundles and leave it for her.

SCENE FOUR

Naomi's house the same evening. Ruth returns, her arms loaded with grain.

RUTH: Look, Naomi. See how much grain I have! And here is some food for you. I was given more than I could eat.

NAOMI: I can't believe it! Where did you glean to find so much? Who gave you the food?

RUTH: The man's name is Boaz. His servant told me I could glean. Then Boaz himself came to the field. He called me to him and told me I was welcome to the grain. He said that I could even drink from the water that was brought for his own workers. Then he gave me food for my lunch—much more than I could eat.

NAOMI: You have found favor with Boaz! He is a kinsman of my husband, a very wealthy man.

RUTH: And a very kind one. He told me to stay close to the women who bind up the grain, and there I would be safe from harm.

NAOMI: This is good news, indeed, my daughter. You must do just as he has told you and glean in his fields every day.

SCENE FIVE

Some days later. The harvest is nearly over. Ruth has been gathering grain in Boaz' field every day. She and Naomi are in the house, talking.

NAOMI: Ruth, I've been thinking about you and your life here in Bethlehem. Shouldn't I find a husband for you so that you will have a home and be happy? Now Boaz is a kinsman of ours. You know that it is our custom that a man must marry his brother's widow. But since your husband's only brother is also dead, perhaps Boaz will marry you.

RUTH: He has been kind to me, but would he be willing to have me as his wife? He would have to buy your property as well, wouldn't he?

NAOMI: I can't be sure that he'll be willing, but he is a good man, and you have found favor in his sight. Tonight he will be winnowing at the threshing floor and will be staying there all night to guard the grain. You must wash and put on your best clothes. Then you must go down to the threshing floor but remain hidden until after the men have finished eating and drinking. Notice where Boaz lies down, and when he is asleep go and lie at his feet. This will tell him that you are willing to be his wife.

RUTH: I will do as you say.

SCENE SIX

Early the next morning. Ruth is returning home to Naomi. Wrapped in her cloak are six measures of grain.

NAOMI: So much grain! (*She reaches out to take it as Ruth hands it to her.*) You must have fared well last night. What did Boaz say?

RUTH: I lay down at his feet just as you told me. When he woke up he asked, "Who are you?" I answered him and reminded him that he was our kin.

NAOMI: And what did he say to that?

RUTH: He seemed pleased. He said I was kind to come to him rather than to seek a husband among the young men.

NAOMI: Will he marry you?

RUTH: He said he would like to because he could tell I was a woman of worth. But he said that there was a nearer kinsman who has first claim on me. Boaz said that he would go to this man to see if he will take me. But if this other kinsman does not wish to buy your property and take me as his wife, Boaz will do so himself.

NAOMI: Good!

RUTH: Before I left him he gave me all this grain, saying that I must not come back to you empty-handed.

NAOMI: He is a good man, Ruth. I hope he will be your husband.

RUTH: He is going to the gate this very day to see the kinsman and meet with the elders to settle this matter.

SCENE SEVEN

The gate where the elders of the city gather and where all disputes among townspeople are settled. Boaz and his kinsman are there, along with the elders.

BOAZ (*turning first to his kinsman and then to the elders*): Sit down here. And you sit down here. Now, my kinsman, you know that Naomi has returned to Bethlehem and that her husband and both sons are dead. Her daughter-in-law, Ruth, is with her. This Moabite woman has left her own people to come with Naomi. Now it is your right as next of kin to buy Naomi's property and to marry Ruth. If you do not wish to do this, tell me, for after you I am next.

KINSMAN: I would be willing to buy the property, but I cannot marry Ruth. Take the right yourself. (*He takes off his sandal and gives it to Boaz.*)

BOAZ (*to the elders*): You are witnesses. My kinsman has given up his right to Ruth, the Moabite, and has taken off his sandal to signify this. You are witnesses also that I have this day bought Naomi's property and also Ruth, the widow of Naomi's son, who will be my wife. In this way I shall continue the name of the dead, for the first son born to Ruth and me shall be counted as the son of her first husband.

ELDERS: We are witnesses. May the Lord make the woman who is coming into your house build up the people of Israel. May you prosper and be renowned in Bethlehem!

SCENE EIGHT

A year later. Naomi is holding a baby in her arms. Several women have gathered around her.

FIRST WOMAN: He is a beautiful child!

NAOMI: Ruth has made me his nurse. She and Boaz count this wonderful baby as if he were my own son. Now I have someone to come after me, to carry on our family line and name.

SECOND WOMAN: God has been good to you.

THIRD WOMAN: Blessed be the Lord who has not left you without next of kin!

FIRST WOMAN: May the Lord's name be renowned in Israel, for he has been good to you; for your daughter-in-law who loves you more than seven sons, has borne a son for you!

The book of Ruth

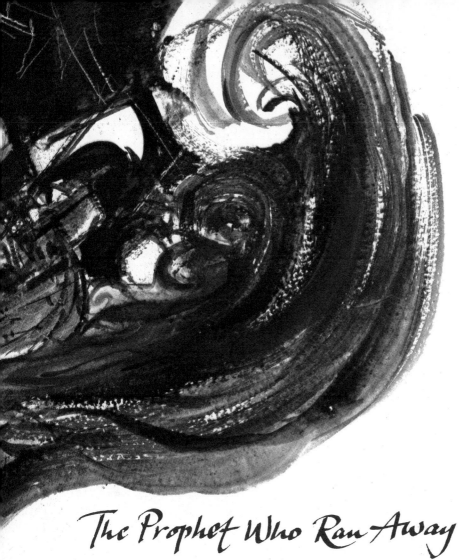

The Prophet Who Ran Away

Now THE WORD of God came to the prophet Jonah, "Arise, go to Nineveh, that great city, and cry out against it. Tell the people that I know their wickedness."

But Jonah did not want to go to Nineveh. It was a long way away, and besides, the people of that wicked city were not Israelites. They *should* be destroyed! If he warned them, they might repent and God might not destroy them after all. Jonah decided he would run away; he would go as far away from God and from Nineveh as he could.

In the city of Joppa he found a ship that was soon to leave for Tarshish. Certain that God would not be able to find him in that distant port, Jonah paid the fare and went on board.

When the ship was out on the sea, God sent a great wind. The ship tossed and bounced on the waves as if it would surely go down. The frightened sailors threw everything they could overboard, and they rowed with all their strength.

Jonah, meanwhile, was asleep below, but the captain found him. "What do you mean, you sleeper?" the captain said. "Get up! Call on your God. Maybe he will listen and save us from perishing in the storm."

Jonah did as he was told, but the storm did not let up. The sailors said to one another, "We must find out who is to blame for this evil. Let us cast lots." So they cast lots to see who had brought evil on the ship, and the lot fell upon Jonah.

The men turned to the prophet and asked, "Who are you and where do you come from?"

Jonah replied, "I am a Hebrew; and I fear the Lord, the God of heaven, who made the sea and the dry land. Right now I am running away from him, because he has sent me to Nineveh, and I don't want to go."

The men became more frightened. If this God were so powerful, and if Jonah had disobeyed him, the ship was indeed in trouble. "What shall we do to make the sea quiet down?" they asked.

"Take me up and throw me into it!" Jonah cried. "Then the sea will quiet down for you."

The men did not want to throw Jonah overboard if they could help it. Instead, they rowed harder and harder to try to bring the ship to land, but they could not. The storm was too wild and the sea too rough.

"Throw Jonah into the sea!" the captain ordered. "We have no choice."

The sailors cried to Jonah's God, "Let us not perish for this man's life!" Then they took Jonah and threw him overboard.

Jonah had scarcely touched the water when the storm stopped. The sailors were amazed. Jonah's God was indeed powerful!

Now God did not want Jonah to drown. He wanted him to go to Nineveh. So he appointed a huge fish to swallow him. For three days and nights Jonah remained in the fish's belly. Then God told the fish to vomit the prophet out on the dry land. The fish did exactly as he was told, and landed Jonah where God wanted him to be.

No sooner was Jonah on his feet than the word of the Lord came to him again, saying, "Arise, go to Nineveh, that great city, and proclaim the message I tell you."

This time Jonah went straight to Nineveh.

Now Nineveh was a very large city, and its wickedness was indeed great. As Jonah looked around, he began to feel a little better. "God will wipe these people out," he said to himself. "There isn't a chance that they'll repent."

When Jonah had gone one day's journey into the city, he began to prophesy. "God will punish you for your wickedness," he cried. "God will overthrow Nineveh. You will perish!"

Jonah began to enjoy the picture that his own words brought to his mind—fire, death to the people, maybe foreign armies attacking. "Just what these people deserve," he thought. His voice grew louder and his words more eloquent as he prophesied. "Doom will come to Nineveh!" he cried. "God will destroy you because of your wickedness!"

Word of the prophet's warning spread quickly over the whole vast city. Immediately the people believed what Jonah was saying and were sorry about their wickedness. Soon the king heard the prophet's words and arose from his throne, took off his robe, and put on sackcloth to mourn over his sins and the sins of his people. The king proclaimed a fast and demanded that everyone turn from his evil ways and ask forgiveness of God. "Who knows," the king thought, "God may change his mind about punishing us if we repent."

Jonah could hardly believe what was happening. He did not expect these wicked people to change. And he did not want them to change! It was bad enough for God to pay attention to this wicked foreign city, but now to have the people of Nineveh pay attention to God was too much. Why, even God's own people, the Israelites, did not often obey him as quickly.

But God's joy was very great when he saw how the people repented and turned away from their evil ways. He took pity on them and decided not to punish them.

Now Jonah was furious. Here he had come all the way to Nineveh to tell the people that God was going to punish them, and now God was not going to punish them! The prophet went outside the city and sat down and sulked.

It was hot sitting there in the sun, and Jonah felt very sorry for himself. When he complained, God took pity on him. Immediately a plant grew up over him and gave him shade. Jonah felt a little better.

But the next day at dawn God appointed a worm to attack the plant and destroy it. The worm did as it was told. Soon the sun began to beat down on Jonah. He was hot and miserable and angry. He wished he were dead. He told God exactly how he felt about everything that had happened to him. "I'm angry enough to die," he said.

God answered him, "You feel sorry about the plant for which you did not labor. You are sorry just because you are uncomfortable without it. But in the city of Nineveh there are a hundred and twenty thousand persons who do not know right from wrong. There are also many cattle. I care about these people. I care about these animals. Should I not, therefore, pity Nineveh and save it from destruction?"

The book of Jonah

HOW TO PRONOUNCE NAMES OF PEOPLE AND PLACES

THE PLAYS ABOUT MOSES: The Man Who Had to Flee His Country and In the Desert

Aaron	ar'un	Moses	mō'ses
Abigail	ab'i-gāl	Nadab	nā'dab
Asher	ash'er	Noah	no'a
Enan	ē'nan	Pharaoh	fā'rō
Hamul	hā'mul	Reuben	rōō'ben
Jethro	jeth'rō	Shemuel	she-mū'el
Laban	lā'ban	Sinai	sī'nī
Midian	mid'i-an	Zipporah	zi-pō'ra

A Faithful Prophet and His Faithful Ass

Amorites	am'o-rīts
Balaam	bā'lam
Balak	bā'lak
Israelite	iz'ri-el-īt
Moab	mō'ab

Joshua Makes a Treaty

Gibeon	gib'e-un
Gilgal	gil'gal
Joshua	josh'ōō-a

THE PLAYS ABOUT DAVID: David Kills the Giant, Two Friends, and David Becomes King

Abiathar	a-bī'a-thar	Gibeah	gib'ē-a
Abinadab	a-bin'a-dab	Goliath	go-lī'ath
Abishai	a-bish'ā-ī	Hebron	hē'bron
Achish	ā'kish	Jabeshgilead	jā'besh-gil'ē-ad
Ahijah	a-hī'ja	Jesse	jes'ē
Amalekite	a-mal'e-kīt	Joab	jō'ab
Amasa	am'a-sa	Philistines	fi-lis'tins
Bethlehem	beth'le-hem	Shammah	sham'a
Eli	ē'lī	Ziklag	zik'lag
Eliab	e-lī'ab	Ziphite	zif'īt

A Man Who Dared to Challenge a King

Ahab	ā'hab	Jezreel	jez'rē-el
Elijah	e-lī'ja	Naboth	nā'both
Jezebel	jez'e-bel	Tyre	tīre

89

"Let Justice Roll Down Like Waters"

Bethel	beth'el
Joel	jō'el
Tekoa	te-kō'a

The King Who Wanted to Obey God

Asherah	a-shē'ra
Assyrians	a-sir'i-ans
Hilkiah	hil-kī'a
Huldah	hūl'da
Jerusalem	je-rōō'sa-lem
Joah	jō'ah
Josiah	jō-sī'ah
Judah	jōō'da
Levites	lē'vīts
Manasseh	ma-nas'e
Nathaniel	na-than'i-el
Shaphan	shā'fan

Thus Says the Lord

Baruch	bar'uk
Jeremiah	jer'e-mī'a

Great-Grandmother to King David

Boaz	bō'az
Mara	ma'ra
Naomi	na-ō'mē
Orpah	or'pa

The Prophet Who Ran Away

Jonah	jō'na
Nineveh	nin'e-ve
Tarshish	tar'shish